HOW AVOID BEING A VICTIM OF THE AMERICAN HEALTHCARE SYSTEM

A Patient's Handbook for Survival

DR. DAVID WILCOX

DNP, MHA, BSN, RN-BC, LSSBB

MW00843439

How to Avoid Being a Victim of the American Healthcare System:
A Patient's Handbook for Survival.

Copyright © 2021 Dr. David Wilcox - All Rights Reserved.

No part of this publication may be reproduced, distributed or transmitted in any form or by any means including photocopying, recording, or other electronic, or mechanical methods, without the prior written permission of the author, except in the case of brief quotations embodied in reviews and certain other non-commercial uses permitted by copyright law.

ISBN: 978-0-578-87836-2

10 9 8 7 6 5 4 3 2 1
Printed in the United States of America

This book is dedicated to my beautiful and loving wife, Eva Wilcox, who has been my editor in chief through four academic degrees and the writing of this book. Without her support I would have never achieved the accomplishments that I have both professionally and personally. When you find your person, love and cherish them as they will be your life partner through all of life's journeys.

Second, I dedicate this book to my mother, M Ann Bird Beetem, and my stepfather, Brant Williams, who always believed in me and supported my crazy journey through academia.

Last, I dedicate this book to my dear sweet aunt Nancy Kubecka, who served as my layperson and assisted me to make this work accessible to the general public. She spent many hours reading and editing my original manuscript to produce the work you are about to read.

DISCLAIMER

This book details the author's personal experiences with and opinions about How to Avoid Being a Victim of the American Healthcare System: A Patient's Handbook for Survival. The author is not your health care provider.

The author and publisher are providing this book and its contents on an "as is" basis and make no representations or warranties of any kind with respect to this book or its contents. The author and publisher disclaim all such representations and warranties, including for example warranties of merchantability and health care for a particular purpose. In addition, the author and publisher do not represent or warrant that the information accessible via this book is accurate, complete, or current due to the changing tide of health care.

Any references to historical events, real people, or real events are based on the author's personal experiences. Names, characters and places have been changed for purposes of protection and anonymity.

The statements made about products and services have not been evaluated by the U.S. Food and Drug Administration. They are not intended to diagnose, treat, cure, or prevent any condition or disease. Please consult with your own physician or health care specialist regarding the suggestions and recommendations made in this book.

Except as specifically stated in this book, neither the author or publisher, nor any authors, contributors, or other representatives will be liable for damages arising out of or in connection with the use of this book. This is a comprehensive limitation of liability that applies to all damages of any kind, including (without limitation) compensatory;

direct, indirect, or consequential damages; loss of data, income, or profit; loss of or damage to property and claims of third parties.

You understand that this book is not intended as a substitute for consultation with a licensed health care practitioner, such as your physician. Before you begin any health care program, or change your lifestyle in any way, you will consult your physician or another licensed health care practitioner to ensure that you are in good health and that the examples contained in this book will not harm you.

This book provides content related to physical and/or mental health issues. As such, use of this book implies your acceptance of this disclaimer.

Contact the author at his website drdavidwilcox.com or his email david@drdavidwilcox.com

CONTENTS

INTRODUCTION

Health care is complex, and that is not an accident. It is a strategy on the part of those who benefit from your health care dollars to keep the general public from knowing what is really going on in the healthcare system. No other business is run the same way. There is little to no transparency, about procedures or billing, and the average health care consumer doesn't think about it until they have to access the healthcare system. That is a dangerous mentality, as we all will need health care at some point in our lives. Not being prepared and knowledgeable means you will have little control over the health care you receive.

If you are reading this, you are already taking a huge step in controlling your health care. In this book, we will be exploring what to do if you have to go to a hospital, how to handle an insurance company's claim denial, how to find an alternative to high-priced prescriptions, and why the current pay-for-fee system is inadequate. You will also discover the direction the healthcare system needs to move towards to holistically care for you, the patient. This is information that the healthcare entities would prefer you didn't know.

As a health care professional, I am amazed by the lack of proactive patient-teaching information available to the general public. Most often health care information is shared with you only after you are diagnosed with a condition. This book is a game changer. When I finished my doctorate I thought: what is the best way that I can arm Americans to navigate the complexities of the healthcare system?

This is why I wrote this book, to educate the average American and possibly save some lives.

Although I am a health care executive these days, at my core I am a nurse. I have been in health care for 28 years, and what you are about to read is based on my experience. I have served as everything from a bedside nurse to a hospital administrator, and I have seen alarming situations that nursing school never prepared me for.

Nursing is a calling. It has also been, for the last 18 years, the number one most trusted profession, according to a 2019 Gallup poll. Of the participants, 85 percent rated a nurse's integrity and honesty as high or very high.[1] As nurses we know how the medical community functions, and we are well versed on how to care for patients. Care is not just physically caring for patients. It also involves emotionally caring and educating patients. As a doctorate prepared nurse, my passion is for my patients, or in this case my readers, to be cared for properly. What you will read in this book will make you better prepared to move through the complex American Healthcare System safely and avoid becoming a victim of it.

While both the doctor and nurse are an essential part of a patient's clinical team, the nurse spends the most time with the patient and therefore has a different perspective. Maybe you know a nurse or have a nurse in the family. Maybe you are a nurse? If so, you understand how involved a nurse can get with their patients and their families.

When nurses are off the clock, we don't stop being nurses. I cannot begin to tell you how many times family and friends have asked me for medical advice. Finding a nurse in your network of family and friends should be an action item that you can work on today.

My wife and I are both nurses. My wife was a hospice nurse at one point in her career while I was a nursing supervisor at our local hospital. As a supervisor part of my responsibilities was to head the code team. A code in medical terms is a situation in which someone's health is severely affected and they could die. You probably have seen emergency room shows where they bring out the code cart, grab the paddles and then shock the patient out of a deadly arrhythmia or heartbeat. Well, the person doing the shocking was usually me, along with the resident physician who was on for the night. My wife, on the other hand, lived in a whole different world. She saw beautiful and tender moments when people were dying. She went into the innermost places of her patient's lives along with their families and was by the bedside for many of her patient's deaths. I can remember when we had a dinner conversation one night and my wife expressed to me," I had two patients pass away today. They died so peacefully and comfortably, it was beautiful to witness." I replied, "Well, I had two patients try to go last night and I shocked the daylights out of them. We coded each one for over an hour, but they lived." As a nurse, you can wear many hats.

Before I became a nursing supervisor, I worked as an intensive care nurse. During this time I had the honor to take care of some extremely sick patients. I can recall one gentleman in particular. I knew his clinical situation was going to be terminal. I was adjusting intravenous (IV) medications just to keep this man alive. As I was doing this particularly important busywork, this gentleman looked straight at me and quietly asked me, "Am I going to die?"

I thought for a moment. In my clinical judgment, I felt this gentleman was not going to make it more than three days. But when faced with a question like that, how do you respond? I gently replied, "Sir you are gravely ill, and to be honest with you I think it would be a miracle if you lived longer than 72 hours." He grasped my hand and looked me straight in the eye. Then he replied, "Thank you for being honest with me." That wonderful gentleman died about 48 hours later. A year later, I saw his wife in the hospital lobby, and she came running up to me. She gave me a big hug and tearfully said, "Thank you for taking care of my husband. He and our daughter had not spoken in 20 years, and after his conversation with you he called her and they made amends." I got teary-eyed and said to myself, "This is why I love being a nurse." My opportunity to go into that innermost sacred space with my patient created a chance for him to make amends and healing between himself and his daughter. While I worked with some great doctors who were managing his care, no one got to walk into that space except his nurse. This is why it is especially important that a nurse takes you through a survival manual and informs you of what you need to know to avoid being a victim of the American Healthcare System.

My hope is you will gain valuable knowledge which will result in your safe and effective care. As a nurse, we are taught to holistically care for our patients' needs. Not just your medical care but your mental well-being and your emotional health too. Let this nurse/doctor take you for a deep dive into the complexities of the American Healthcare System and break it down into layperson's terms, giving you the knowledge and tools you need to survive it.

<u>*Part 1*</u>

Staying
Safe
Inside
the
Hospital

CHAPTER 1

What to Know Before You Go to the Hospital

No one enjoys going to the hospital, but sometimes it's a necessity. A hospital stay means a loss of your independence and submitting yourself to being in a different environment on a different schedule than your normal routine. If you have a condition that can be better managed in a setting where you have access to 24/7 medical professionals, then going to the hospital is a no-brainer. Having pain shooting through your right groin area, only to find out that you have a ruptured appendix, warrants a trip to the hospital for an appendectomy (removal of the appendix) and then monitoring to make sure you do not have complications such as a blood infection known as sepsis.

If a medical professional tells you that treatment for your condition should occur in a monitored environment such as a hospital, then you probably should go. If you are unsure, you can always get a second opinion—if it's not an emergency. Doctors generally do not like to send their patients to the hospital as a rule if they can be treated in an alternative setting. Many times your doctor may not be the one in charge of your care in the hospital. It may be a hospitalist who oversees your care. A hospitalist is a doctor who specializes in caring for patients in a hospital setting. The hospitalist will study your chart to learn your history but will not know you as well as your attending doctor, so communication with the hospitalist will be key. Ask your doctor if they will be overseeing your care or using a hospitalist.

If your appendix was inflamed and hadn't ruptured, you may be sent to an ambulatory surgical center (ASC) where it can be removed and you can go home to recover. That would be one way to have an appendix removed. If your doctor is suggesting that you go to the hospital, talk to the doctor about other options such as an ASC.

If you have the luxury of time, meaning your hospital stay isn't an emergency, research your condition to better understand what you can expect during your hospital stay. This will also decrease your anxiety about being outside your home environment and let you know exactly what to expect during your hospital stay.

The internet is like the wild west when it comes to medical advice. You should start with reputable sites such as WebMD https://www.webmd.com/. There are also site-specific websites depending on your condition. One good example is facty.com, which describes the procedure you are having done. For a cardiac catheterization, they inform you that the interventional cardiologist will be inserting a catheter through a large artery to diagnosis your heart problem and may even place stents to open clogged arteries and allow blood to flow to your heart more rapidly. The more you know about your condition and what to expect at a hospital the better partner you will be to your health care team.

NURSING KNOWLEDGE

Most patients think that their doctor will be caring for them in the hospital setting. Usually, the duties are assigned to a hospitalist. Ask your doctor how he will be monitoring your health and receiving information if he is working with a hospitalist. Be specific, ask the doctor how often he will be communicating with the hospitalist, as your doctor understands your health care situation the best. Ask if they will talk by phone (preferred) or if he will be getting daily reports. Keep your doctor involved in your care.

Choosing the Hospital

Choosing your hospital and your physician are especially important steps if you must go to the hospital. There are all kinds of data out there that will let you know how your hospital fares as compared to the national benchmarks. National benchmarks are standards that the Centers for Medicare & Medicaid Services (CMS) have set for issues like infection rates and never events. A never event is something that CMS believes should never occur under any situation in health care. There is a wealth of data located at Data.Medicare.gov, which can be accessed at the following link https://data.medicare.gov/ [2] This is best accessed from a personal computer or laptop. Simply click on the https://www.medicare.gov/care-compare/ button below the word "search" to get started. The hospital in my emergency department story, which we will discuss later, was only rated two stars out of five, and having experienced care there, I now know why.

The data allows you to compare hospitals, compare physicians, and even compare long-term care centers. This is important because unless you do your research you could end up being sicker when you come out of the hospital than when you went in. It is worth your time to look at a hospital's infection rate. For instance, if you're going in for a surgical procedure and you see that a hospital's infection rate is worse than the rest of the country, and you discover the surgeon who's going to perform the surgery on you has a high infection rate, you probably want to look for another hospital and another surgeon.

A little-known fact outside the medical community is while your surgeon works on you in the operating room, it is the anesthesiologist who is charged with keeping you alive. But as with most things in health care, this is complex, as your anesthesiologist may not be in the room during your surgery. Instead, the anesthesiologist may be overseeing a Certified Registered Nurse Anesthetist (CRNA), which isn't necessarily bad, but you should know so you can assemble the best health care team to make sure you receive the optimal care. Remember, you are hiring these experts to look after you during a time in which you will not be conscious or able to weigh in on their decisions, so do your homework and gather as much information as possible. Ask the anesthesiologist if they will be doing the procedure or if it will be a CRNA. You want to know who is keeping you alive during your surgery.

One way to ensure you are hiring quality individuals on your medical team is to use the Data.Medicare.gov site to look up your anesthesiologist or any team member by asking in advance for their name.

Do Your Research

Like anything else you will encounter in life, some people in health care excel at what they do and some do not. The difference is those who do not excel in taking care of their patients can cause harm. While hiring a bad plumber may cause some water damage in your house, hiring a bad surgeon can cost you a long recovery time or possibly even death. The typical patient does not understand they have total control over which doctor cares for them. Sure, there are barriers such as the doctor being in their health insurance network, which means they will pay less out of pocket money, but if you have a doctor who is outside of your network and is the best at what they do, they may be worth the additional expense.

When you are a nurse at a hospital, you pretty much know what surgeons or doctors you would allow to care for your family. That is a huge advantage because you have seen their mistakes and you have seen good outcomes. Many patients do not have this firsthand experience. I can remember one time when I was out grocery shopping, I overheard two women having a conversation. One announced to the other, "Oh yes, I'm going to the hospital Monday, and doctor so and so is going to operate on me."

Now, I had taken care of this doctor's patients, and many of them did not do well after their surgeries. There was a marked difference between other surgeon's patient outcomes and this particular surgeon's patient outcomes. In other words, this was a surgeon I would not let come within 100 feet of myself or any of my family members. Finding a good, honest mechanic is something we all try to do. This is much more important when choosing a surgeon, doctor, or hospital.

In the medical community poor performing people sometimes are allowed to continue to practice. That is why hospital systems are moving from getting paid for the number of patients they see to getting paid on the patients' quality outcomes. My conscience bothered me as I continued to shop in the store. I struggled, asking myself if it would be ethical for me to say something to this woman and if so, I could not tell her who I am.

Lo and behold, this woman appeared with her grocery cart coming down the same aisle I was in. I always believe in doing what is right and took this as a sign, so as she came down the aisle I spoke softly, "I couldn't help but overhear your conversation about your operation that you are having Monday. I can't tell you who I am, but I am going to tell you that you should change your surgeon." She looked at me wide-eyed and I responded, "I can't say anymore, but I work at the hospital, and you should find a different doctor."

As I started to walk away I heard her say thank you. It is so important to do your research on your physician and your hospital. If you do not do your research, you may risk putting yourself in a precarious situation.

NURSING KNOWLEDGE

Do your research! You wouldn't buy a car without checking on its safety rating or researching how much you would pay for the car. Health care should be no different. Find the best hospital and doctor in your area. This will give you much better odds of having a safe experience and get you on to the road to recovery.

Medications

Most patients are under the assumption that the health care team consults with each other on the patient's care, but that is not always the case. Medications are a huge part of your care, and safely administering them, plus reconciling them with your other drugs when the doctor orders new medications, is when many errors occur. Reconciling medications is usually done in the electronic medical record (EMR) system by a doctor. It happens when you are admitted, change a venue of care such as going from surgery to a unit bed, and upon discharge. This process was carried out badly when medical personnel still used paper, and the automation of this process isn't much better.

It's very important because you want to be getting the correct dose, the correct medication, and the correct way the medication should be administered. For instance, when you have surgery, many times the surgeon does not want to reconcile your daily medications. Instead, they want to just order what you need in the recovery period and let your attending doctor or hospitalist write orders for your daily medications. Sometimes the recovery nurse doesn't discontinue your recovery medications, and they follow you to the next venue of care, such as the inpatient floor. Behind the scenes, medication management in the hospital can be a disaster.

One thing you can do to avoid an issue is pack up all your medications before going to the hospital. A better practice is listing your medications in a computer file and printing off multiple copies. Give each caregiver that you interact with—doctor, nurse, anesthesiologist, etc.—a copy of your medications. Do not assume that your team is communicating with each other about your medications. Take control of this situation and communicate the medications that you take, including any supplements.

I had an uncle who had phosphorus problems and hospitals did not stock his medications all the time, so he simply brought his medications from home when he had to go to the hospital. The hospital pharmacy disliked this, as they have to go through a rigorous process to verify the medications. But at the end of the day, it's not about what the pharmacy likes or doesn't like; it's all about keeping you safe. This is an option that many patients do not know they have. If you are going to be admitted to the hospital, bring in your home medications and request they be used instead of medications from the pharmacy. It may even save you some money.

Health care in this country is moving away from an approach in which we provide care to the patients in a top-down fashion. What I mean by that is in the past the physician was the keeper of all knowledge, and there was little input from patients. That is changing as patients do their research, using the Internet, and start to ask questions. This new approach allows you as a patient to have a say in your health care.

Using the knowledge you have gained from this chapter will help you safely navigate the healthcare system and be in better control of your care. Although you will be out of your normal element, you can still retain control of key factors like hiring the best possible health care team, choosing a hospital that delivers quality care, and managing your medications. Research is key as well as communication with your health care team to ensure you have an optimal experience while in the hospital. While it's rare that someone looks forward to going to the hospital, an informed patient can provide themselves a degree of safety that an uninformed patient cannot.

NURSING KNOWLEDGE

Medication management is crucial. If an error occurs in a hospital, it usually concerns medication administration. Bringing in a list of your current medications is important but having your nurse read back to you the medications listed in the electronic medical record (EMR) is very important. If you change venues of care, such as going to surgery and then to an inpatient room, the first thing you should do is ask your nurse to read your medications back to you from the EMR to ensure they are correct.

CHAPTER 2

Tips on Surviving Your Hospital Experience

....

Walking into the hospital, you will likely meet with a registrar who will record your information, including your insurance information. Bring a copy of your health care proxy and living will, if you have them, to include in your medical record. While this person is not a doctor or a nurse, give them as much information as possible. Once they have gathered the information, you will be escorted to the inpatient floor or taken to the surgical area.

Going to the hospital can be an intimidating experience. I have admitted many patients to the hospital and I have seen the anxiety and fear in their eyes. This is because these patients did not know what to expect. Preparing yourself for the hospital experience is the best way to understand what will happen there.

When you are admitted to the hospital you lose a lot of independence. You may be hooked up to intravenous (IV) lines. You have to eat at certain times of the day. You're dependent on others for your care. You lose a great deal of your privacy. Knowing you will need to be somewhat flexible about your routine is key to having the correct expectations during your hospital stay. Remember that your nurse may be caring for many patients and some of them may be sicker than you are and require more attention.

Many times you are required to wear a "hospital gown" that leaves your entire backside exposed, bruising your sense of dignity. Asking hospital staff if you can wear your own pajamas will help you feel more comfortable and more in control. They may say no, but it doesn't hurt to ask.

You may find yourself in unfamiliar noisy surroundings. Let's face it, not a lot of people go to the hospital to catch up on sleep. Being prepared for this means you may need to ask for sleep medication or alter your sleeping pattern by taking more naps during the day. You can also ask that no one takes your vital signs during the night if they are within a normal range, such as no fever, heart rate is normal and blood pressure is within normal limits. If your vital signs are not normal, then do not request they are not taken at night. Your nurse should be able to help you navigate this issue and arrive at the best decision for your care.

You may get a grouchy nurse, or you may have a doctor that does not allow you the opportunity to ask questions because they are moving so quickly and do not seem to have additional time for you. This is because the doctors are pressed into seeing many patients throughout the day and may be working until late in the evening. The schedule isn't any easier for the nurses. Often when interacting with an individual such as a nurse or doctor who may be a little gruff, a good approach is saying "Wow, you must be having a really bad day because this can't be the way you normally interact with people. Is there anything I can do to help?" This usually causes the person to think about their behavior and usually remedies the situation. Some clinical staff likes to feel in control, but the bottom line is you are paying their salaries and you are the one in control of your health. You may be dependent on them during your stay, but if you are having a problem with an individual, ask to speak to the unit manager during the day or the nursing supervisor after hours.

While in the hospital you will interact with various individuals. Besides doctors and nurses, there will be nurse techs who perform duties such as taking your vital signs or setting you up for meals. You may have transporters who take you for an X-ray or a CAT scan. Most patients who do not feel well have to work very hard to have a good disposition. Just as in life, relationships with your care team are everything. If your nurse is rushed, touching their hand and saying,

"I can wait if you have more pressing duties" sends an empathic message saying we are a team.

People become nurses because they are caring individuals for the most part. This was very apparent during the recent pandemic when nurses literally put their lives on the line to care for members of their communities who often were not following basic precautions such as wearing a mask or practicing social distancing. A good patient understands that a nurse is caring for several patients and only has a certain amount of time that they can spend with them. Creating a good relationship with a nurse tech and even an environmental services (EVS) person who cleans your room and empties the trash will enhance your hospital stay, as often they will make more time to devote to the little things that can make your stay better. Things like getting hospital slippers or asking to move to a chair while you have intravenous (IV) lines and IV pumps attached are duties the nurse tech can provide. An EVS person can refill your water pitcher or score you an extra pillow. Relationships matter in the hospital just as they do in life and the hospital staff always enjoy patients that are willing to work with them. This creates a caregiver bond, and once you become a favorite patient, the staff will frequently go out of their way to make sure you have everything you need to be comfortable during your hospital stay.

NURSING KNOWLEDGE

No nurse likes a grumpy patient. Nurses have a lot of duties so conducting yourself as a team player is key to getting what you need in a hospital. You can ask not to be awakened in the night for vital signs but if your nurse thinks that's a bad idea listen to the reason why. Nurses love patients who take part in their care while listening to sound medical advice.

Avoiding Infections

In the year 2000, a reported 2.4 million people died in hospitals in the United States. In 2010 that number rose to more than 2.5 million. Between 2000 and 2010 septicemia or blood infections increased 17 percent. [3] The hospital can be a dangerous and unpleasant environment. Not because the doctors and the nurses are incompetent, but because the clinical staff is overloaded and must take care of many patients. They are usually understaffed due to the chronic nursing shortage and although they try to do their best to keep up with their heavy workload, sometimes mistakes are made. Why do they have to take care of so many patients at the same time? While there are many variables, one of the biggest is insurance/payors, which control the reimbursement models or how a hospital gets paid. This will be addressed later in the book.

You can acquire many different types of infections as a patient in a hospital. The hospitals are like Petri dishes, as there are a lot of germs floating around despite the best cleaning efforts. Without proper precautions, germs can be passed from patient to patient pretty easily. Most hospitals have protocols in place to keep you safe, but it is up to the individual clinician to practice them.

One of the biggest steps you can take to ensure your safety from these infections is to make sure anyone who comes in contact with you—doctor, nurse, physical therapist, occupational therapist, even your family members— washes their hands for 20 seconds or more before coming near you. This precaution has been proven to cut down the infection rate. If a clinician taking care of you approaches and you haven't seen them thoroughly wash their hands, you have the right to ask them to wash their hands. Some people are afraid or not comfortable asking a clinician to do that, but it is an essential behavior to keep you safe, and it is a procedure you can control.

Rapid Response Nurses

Recognizing that early intervention saves lives, a program that began in Australia caught fire in the United States. The Institute of Healthcare Improvement (IHI) ran a save a hundred thousand lives campaign to reduce hospital deaths. This initiative really moved forward in the early 2000's. The guidelines mandated that a hospital system of greater than three hundred beds should have a dedicated 24/7 nurse resource in a rapid response role. A hospital with less than 300 beds should have an intensive care nurse (ICU) on call to manage rapid response events. The other members of the health care team assigned to the rapid response team (RRT) are the resident physician covering the hospital and a respiratory therapist. In Australia, they found that by implanting an RRT team, they were able to significantly reduce codes, or life-threatening events, outside the ICU unit.

While I was working at the hospital, I helped set up an RRT program. An intensive care unit (ICU) trained nurse would walk the units, rounding or checking on newer nurses and asking how their patients were doing. This allowed the newer nurses to have an expert available in case something was not right. Perhaps they had just a gut feeling or maybe a change in the patient's vital signs. Either way, they had this nurse resource to call before the person coded and wound up in an ICU bed.

What we found was after the initiation of this nursing position, we were able to reduce the number of codes that occurred outside an ICU by 50 percent over a two year period. That means half of the emergencies occurring outside an ICU were addressed before they became code situations. The rapid response nursing program was keeping patients safer and saving more lives.

When resources were being crunched—in other words, when there were not enough nurses—administrators considered pulling the rapid response nurse back to the ICU to address the staffing crisis. I told the lead nurse over the rapid response team program that this day may come. I had her keep track of code data and where the codes were occurring. One thing hospital administrators understand is money. We put a dollar figure to the data, and we were able to show them how much money we were saving the organization by catching these codes before they occurred. This ended the conversation about pulling that valuable nursing resource back into the ICU and eliminating that rapid response nurse position.

A good question for you to ask when you are inquiring about a hospital is, "Do you have a rapid response program"? Or in smaller hospitals that may not be able to support a rapid response nurse position, you might ask, "What is your process to intervene before a patient's condition deteriorates such as if their vital signs become unstable and a patient's condition looks worse"?

NURSING KNOWLEDGE

Handwashing is extremely important! Make sure everyone you come in contact with, family or staff, washes their hands. Ask how the hospital handles a patient whose condition is deteriorating. That way you know what to expect. You can ask to meet the rapid response nurse if that position exists and ask them how often they will be checking on you. This establishes a relationship with that nurse and lets them know you want to be an active member in your health care.

Learning and Surveys

Health care professionals have a lot of knowledge, and part of the requirements of hospital policy is that the clinical staff must attempt to educate you on your disease process. When you are in the hospital, though, teaching usually occurs at your discharge.

During a hospital stay and especially at discharge most of the patients are very tired due to sleep deprivation, and the last thing they want to do is take in information. Most of them just want to leave and get back home. The nurse rushes in with a lot of paperwork, and the patients nod their heads and sign anything just to get the heck out of the hospital.

This has been an ineffective process or way of teaching patients for many years. It has never worked well. If you find yourself in the hospital with a newly acquired condition, ask your nurse for information on it. They usually have patient teaching materials in their electronic medical record which they can print out and give to you well in advance of your discharge. This allows you to learn when you are ready to receive the information, and ask questions when you run across something you do not understand. This will make you better prepared and more knowledgeable about what you should do to avoid another hospital stay.

Lastly, you will get a survey in the mail asking about your experience at the hospital. If you had a nurse, doctor, or other staff members that knocked it out of the park, please mention them on your survey. Do take the time to fill the survey out, as the hospital may not know about their star players. If your experience wasn't good, they can't improve it for the next patient if they do not know where they missed the mark. This survey is also a part of their reimbursement structure, or the money they make from your hospital stay. It is part of the hospital's rating system, which we will discuss later in the book. Now let's talk about medications.

CHAPTER 3

Medication Madness

According to a report, medical errors are the third leading cause of death in the United States. [4] Medication errors, or as the industry calls them—adverse drug events—occur to nearly five percent of the patients in the hospital. This makes them one of the most common errors in the medical field. [5] This is pretty disturbing, especially if you do not know what to look for in those situations. Being a nurse gives me an advantage, and I want you to understand the advantage fully so that if you do have to go to the hospital you know exactly what to expect and what your role is in the process.

Ask Questions and Observe the Process

Before you ever take a medication in the hospital you need to ask the nurse the name of the medication and question what the medication is for. It is tricky because medications have multiple names. They have brand names and they have generic names at a minimum. So what you are used to taking at home may be referred to by a different name at the hospital. A good example is Tylenol, which is the drug's brand name. The generic name for Tylenol is acetaminophen and the intravenous version of the drug is named Paracetamol. Even though it is the same drug, it can be referred to by up to three different names. It is okay to keep asking questions until you understand it is a drug you usually take or it is a new drug and question what the drug is for.

Most hospitals use technology to help provide safe patient care. Your nurse should come in the room and scan your wristband and then scan the medications to match the medications to you, the patient. If this does not occur, you should ask if the hospital uses the technology. If the hospital does, tell them you would be more comfortable with them scanning the medications in front of you before administering them. I cannot tell you how many times I have seen nurses print off an extra armband and use it to scan medications in the medication room. You might be thinking this is not a big deal. But if you are carrying many patients' armbands and the nurse is in a hurry, this is a medication error waiting to happen.

Medication errors can often increase the amount of time you are in the hospital, which will increase your bill. The process of scanning medications at the bedside in front of the patient is a best practice for patient safety. This is especially important with intravenous medications or IV medications.

I can recall a situation when I was supporting a conversion of an electronic medical record system (EMR). A conversion of an EMR is when you first turn on the system and clinical staff have to get used to it while caring for patients, it can be very stressful and disruptive. Being a nurse, I was supporting the emergency department in this hospital, and when I walked into the emergency department, I was accosted by the nursing staff. They wanted to know if I thought it was acceptable for them to be scanning medications in a code situation. Now, you remember a code is a serious medical emergency. My answer to them was in a code situation, medical staff must do what they have to do to keep the patient alive. If that means they do not scan, then they do not scan the medications. This is an industry standard.

One of the nurses announced, "Well, I am just not going to scan my medications. I don't have time for this and I don't need to do it." I asked her if I could follow her while she was giving medications to a patient and she reluctantly agreed. When we went into the patient's room this nurse was getting ready to start an intravenous or IV antibiotic. I asked the patient if I could observe the medication administration process. After obtaining the patient's permission I asked the nurse to please scan the antibiotic before she hung it. She rolled her eyes at me, picked up the scanner and scanned the patient's armband, and then scanned the medication. All of a sudden an alert came up in the electronic medical record which stated the patient was allergic to that antibiotic. That was what you call an ah-ha moment.

Now let's go back to the reason why she did not want to scan. She thought it would cost her more time working with the technology than caring for the patient. As a nurse, I get that. But what she did not realize had she hung that antibiotic and the patient had an allergic reaction, she was going to spend a lot more time with that patient pulling them out of a possible anaphylactic shock, which is a deadly allergic reaction that if left untreated could cause the patient's airway to swell and close off.

So, remember when you are in the hospital, do not allow the staff to take shortcuts. Make sure you hold them accountable because that's when mistakes happen. If your nurse is rushed, ask them to come back when things are calmer. Remember that medication errors happen to approximately five percent of all patients in the hospital, so if an error is going to happen to you, there is a strong chance it will center around medications.

You also want to be aware of any medical complications you have had in the past. This is especially true with surgery, as you will be incapacitated and relying on others caring for you. One patient that went from the operating room (OR) to the recovery room after a routine surgery immediately started having seizures. The staff were dumbfounded and could not figure out what was going on. The head of the department of anesthesia had to call a hospital many states away, where the patient had their last procedure and found out the patient had the same reaction to anesthesia at that hospital. I do not know if they told her about this reaction and she forgot, but that is pretty important information to give to your anesthesiologist.

If you have a surgical procedure under anesthesia, you should ask how you did with the anesthesia and record that information somewhere to use at a later date. The more information your health care team has, the better your outcome will be.

Since we are on the topic of surgery, here is another valuable piece of information to know, especially if you are a self-paying patient (one without insurance). Recovery time at most hospitals is charged by the minute. If your nurse and you feel like you're ready to be discharged from the recovery room, you should move to a unit bed or be discharged as soon as possible to avoid any additional expense.

Medications During an Emergency Department Visit

Sometimes you have to rush to the emergency room due to a medical crisis such as a heart attack or stroke. At times like these, do not take time to gather up your current medications, as time is of the essence. You can, however, carry a list of your current medications in your wallet or purse so that you will always have it with you. Another possibility is taking a picture of your list of medications and storing them on your phone.

This emergency department experience will show you the importance of knowing your medications and properly communicating them to your care team. I woke up one morning and noticed that I had a lump right above my right nipple. This area was red, sore, and tender to the touch. Being a nurse, I strongly suspected I was beginning to develop an abscess. About 24 hours later, I started to develop shivering chills and knew that I might be developing sepsis. That is a blood infection, which was due to the abscess. My wife immediately took me to our local emergency department.

When we arrived, the place was extremely busy. I was registered at the front desk and was asked to sit in the waiting room to be triaged. Triage means that somebody decides who is the sickest and they are seen by the medical staff first. I did not have a particularly long wait before I saw the triage nurse and physician's assistant.

I was told because of my fever they would need to draw blood and culture it. Yet I was given two Tylenol to take before my blood draw, which is a big nursing no-no. Tylenol should not be given before drawing blood cultures, as it can affect the cultures' results by decreasing the fever. Tylenol is only given after the blood cultures are completed. l was also told that I would be given an antibiotic. This is important as the faster you get an antibiotic in a blood infection situation, the better the outcome for the patient.

I was moved to the laboratory area and the nurse drew my blood. He also said that he needed to go to the medication dispensing machine and get my antibiotic. He was gone quite a long time and when he returned he said that there was an issue in the pharmacy and the antibiotic that I had been prescribed was not in the machine. He directed me back to the waiting room and said somebody would bring the antibiotic relatively soon. I did not receive the antibiotic until six hours later when the triage nurse brought it to me. In the meantime, the Tylenol wore off and I was right back to having a fever and chills.

When I finally saw the doctor, it was seven hours later. Remember that triage situation I discussed earlier? It turns out that they had several ambulances come in with some extremely sick patients so that increased my wait time.

The doctor had a wonderful bedside manner. The doctor had to cut open my abscess and drain it, so he gave me some pain medication. The nurse also gave me another two Tylenol. Upon discharge, the nurse attempted to have me take another dose of the antibiotic they had given me just two hours ago.

Being a nurse, I knew this was clearly a medication error. I asked the nurse to check the electronic medical record (EMR) to see when my last dose was given. She could not find that information in their EMR. This is why I say clinicians are often overworked and sometimes make mistakes.

The two errors were: the first nurse forgot to chart the antibiotic, causing the second nurse to offer the medication to me because the doctor ordered it. Another miss was the doctor told me that he was going to send me home with a prescription for some pain medication. At discharge, I noticed I had not been given the prescription and had to ask for it. Had I not known about pain medication management and if I was not a nurse, I might have taken that second antibiotic and left without my pain medication prescription.

NURSING KNOWLEDGE

If an error is going to occur in a hospital it usually is a medication administration error. Always ask about your medications and do not be passive while they are being administered. An informed patient who participates in their care is a safe patient. Be present and know what each medication is for. Don't be afraid to ask questions.

Take Your Medications

A startling 26 percent of patients who are readmitted to the hospital return because they are not taking their medications correctly. This can be because they can't afford the medication or they don't like the effects of the medication and simply choose to stop taking it.

That can be a severe problem with chronic diseases. For instance, hypertension is a silent killer. It is the single most common risk factor for cardiovascular disease. Yet there are no obvious effects of the disease. No one has a bad day from hypertension, such as feeling bad like one would with the flu. For that reason, many times people do not adhere to their hypertension medication regime. Often hypertensive medications have side effects like dizziness, due to interactions with other medications or because the dose is too high. Oftentimes people just stop taking their hypertensive medication without understanding the impact on their total health care picture. High blood pressure weakens the arterial walls and if left untreated can cause a stroke or a rupture of the artery, causing a person to bleed to death. Working with your medical team to find a medication that works for you and doesn't have side effects is a must.

My 84 year old mother had a bad heart. Over the years she had 11 stents placed in her arteries to keep them open, and she was not a good candidate for open heart surgery, according to her cardiologist. Even if she was, having open heart surgery entails a long, slow recovery and was not a procedure she wanted to go through at 84 years old. She did well on the stents for many years, but over the past year, she became extremely fatigued. Walking was hard, as she became very short of breath. The event that led us to seek additional care for her was on a trip she and my stepfather took out of state in which they stopped at a local Walmart. They walked to the back of the store, where she accidentally left her sunglasses. She had to go back to the store to retrieve the sunglasses. When she came back to the car, her husband noticed she was extremely short of breath. My mother was not always medically compliant. She had nitroglycerin pills with her, which dilate the coronary arteries to improve blood flow to her heart. I had told her many times when she started to get short of breath to pop one of those nitro's and see if it helped.

She popped three of those nitros after this incident with a little bit of relief. So, we decided to explore other options for her and see what else we could do, as her quality of life was deteriorating. Her cardiologist had her seen by one of the best interventional cardiologists in the world, who performed a catheterization on her. The doctor opened a clogged artery, which made my mother feel better for the remaining days of her life.

Taking your medications and discussing side effects with your medical team is essential. If a medication makes you feel bad, often you can take another medication that won't. Many times my mother would stop or decrease the dose of her medications because of the way it made her feel. She would never tell me about it. Instead, she confided in my sister, who immediately reported it to me. I would call her to find out why she wasn't taking the medication, which was usually a valid reason, and then we would discuss it with her primary care doctor who would change the medication to reduce the side effects. We all have different metabolisms, and what works for me may not necessarily work for you. Open and honest communication with your care team and discussing how your medications are making you feel is the key to living your best life under any condition.

NURSING KNOWLEDGE

Your care team are not mind readers. If you are prescribed a medication that makes you feel bad, you have to report it so the doctor can get you on a different medication. Not taking your medications should not be an option, as it will negatively impact your health.

CHAPTER 4

What You Should Know About Surgery

Many people come to the hospital because they need an operation. When you do your initial consultation with your surgeon, ask him if the surgery can be done at an ambulatory surgical center (ASC). It used to be only certain surgeries could be done at an ASC, but with the advances in modern medicine, that list is expanding. The Centers for Medicare and Medicaid Services (CMS) has a list of Inpatient Only Procedures. These are procedures that must be done at the hospital. You can find this list on the CMS website.

For example, in 2018 CMS moved total knee arthroplasty off that list which opened up the possibility of having this surgery at an ambulatory surgical center. Many times having surgery done at an ASC lowers the cost dramatically.

There are trade-offs for having surgery at an ASC instead of a hospital and you should discuss the pros and cons with your surgeon. If you have comorbidities, meaning you have medical conditions such as high blood pressure, diabetes, or congestive heart failure, the surgeon may insist on doing the surgery at a hospital, as it may take you longer to heal. If it's possible to have the surgery at an ASC and the surgeon is okay with it, by all means, have your surgery done there. Most of the time you will go home the same day, with a lot more money in your pocket.

What to Ask Your Surgeon

Earlier in the book, I advised that you check your surgeon's quality ratings. You may have had a consultation with the surgeon and think the surgeon has a wonderful bedside manner, but the data does not lie. Another thing you can do is if you know a nurse at the hospital or ASC, ask them about your surgeon. If you don't know one, ask your network of friends to see if anyone does. Nurses want people to have good outcomes and should be honest about the surgeon's skill set.

Once you have determined where you will have your surgery and you have found a good-quality surgeon, you will meet with the surgeon for a consultation. Here are some questions that you should ask.

The first thing you should ask is how many times your surgeon has performed this surgery. You don't want to be any surgeon's first patient, right? Then ask if any of the surgeon's patients had complications and if so, has death ever occurred from this type of surgery? Don't be surprised if they say yes. Many good surgeons have lost people because they came to the hospital in critical condition and the surgeon was trying to save their lives. But it's good to know as many details of the situation as the surgeon is willing to share.

Many years ago I lived in a town with two competing hospitals. One of them cherry-picked the patients that they were willing to do open heart surgery on. They took the easy patients that needed a one- or two-vessel bypass surgery and were in relatively good shape. This allowed them to keep their CMS star ratings up. The other, which was a state hospital, took the hard patients. They often needed three or more vessel bypass surgery and often had comorbidities such as obesity, diabetes, and high blood pressure. While the CMS star ratings were higher at the first hospital, the skill set of the surgeons at the state hospital were much better. We all knew what was going on, but the community did not. For all intents and purposes, it would appear that you should have your open heart surgery at the first hospital, but the surgeons at the state-run hospital knew how to deal with complications better than those at the first hospital. That's why it's important to have a local nurse in your network of friends.

Ask your surgeon when you will be on his surgery schedule. Ideally, you want to be the first case of the day, as after midnight the night before you will not be able to eat or drink. Waiting all day for surgery while starved is a miserable experience. Plus, being first means the surgeon should be well rested and ready to operate. Being last on the list, after the surgeon has had a long day, means the surgeon may be tired and not as mentally sharp.

Another question you should ask is how often the surgeon is on call. Being on call means that the surgeon is covering for himself or his practice and may be getting woken up frequently to give patient orders or having to go to the hospital during the night. This means they may not be well rested when he or she performs your surgery.

Ask your surgeon what the recovery period is for your surgery. How long will you be in the hospital? This alleviates anxiety and helps you plan your recovery time. Ask about how much pain you will be in during the recovery period. If you are sensitive to pain, make sure the surgeon knows that so they can plan your recovery care adequately.

The other thing that you want to ask your surgeon is, "Will you be doing the surgery on me?" You would think this is a no-brainer, but many times at teaching hospitals a resident performs the actual surgery under the surgeon's guidance. You have the right to ask the surgeon if they will be performing the actual surgery. Residents do have to learn how to do surgery, but your surgeon has many more years of experience and knowledge, so be very clear that you want your surgeon to do the actual surgery.

If you know someone who recommends any member of the health care team, including nurses, doctors, surgeons, nurse techs, etc., and they work on the inpatient unit or the recovery room, you can ask to be taken care of by them. Most hospitals will try to accommodate your request, as it is all about the patient experience. Remember the survey we talked about earlier in the book? Every hospital system wants to have good CMS star ratings and should work with you to accommodate your request.

The Crappy Cardiologist

Cardiac procedures have come a long way. With the introduction of cardiac catheterizations and the use of stents, open heart surgery has decreased dramatically. Stents open a clogged artery, allowing the blood to flow freely. Before the use of stents, open heart surgery was a patient's only alternative.

Many years ago pacemakers were bulky and hard to manage. Through making a small incision into the chest wall, it is now possible to have an indwelling pacemaker or defibrillator, or both. This allows a patient to lead a normal life, and the batteries may last for up to seven years, depending on the use. But like all battery-operated devices sometimes they can fail.

While serving as a hospital supervisor one evening we had a patient in an intensive care unit (ICU) who had a pacemaker/defibrillator unit implanted in his chest. These are frequently used to regulate the patient's heart rate and deliver a shock if they go into a lethal arrhythmia or deadly rhythm. I was called to the ICU because this patient was going into a lethal arrhythmia and was being shocked by his indwelling defibrillator to break the lethal arrhythmia. The defibrillator had shocked the patient multiple times, and the patient's nurse was very concerned. I told the nurse to call the cardiologist on call.

This particular cardiologist took major risks in the cardiac catheterization lab. Some of his patients had suffered a stroke after certain procedures he performed on them. Plus, he had a nasty attitude and thought he was above everyone. A good doctor or nurse understands the value of teamwork, but this particular individual wanted to call all the shots. This occurred before you could check the doctor's quality ratings, but the majority of the hospital staff knew this doctor was a loose cannon and his patients did not do as well as the other cardiologists' patients.

I stood by for the phone call and could overhear the doctor telling this relatively new nurse to place a magnet over the implanted defibrillator. A magnet placed over a pacemaker/defibrillator will shut it off. This is far outside of the scope of practice for a nurse and dangerous if not done in the proper setting. The nurse said to me, "He wants me to put a magnet on his pacemaker/defibrillator unit."

I asked the nurse to give me the phone. I told the doctor that there was no way we were going to put a magnet on this pacemaker/defibrillator, as it was doing exactly what it was supposed to be doing, and it would be dangerous to turn it off. "I am giving you a direct order" he yelled at me.

I replied, "And I am refusing it." Nurses can refuse doctor's orders if they feel it would be harmful to the patient. I then said, "You need to come in and see this patient, and if you don't I am going to call the Chief Medical Officer!" I hung the phone up with him still yelling at me.

Through this whole ordeal, the patient was awake and aware of what was happening. The patient was scared, rightfully so. Eventually, the cardiologist arrived and made a particularly grand entrance, he was mad because he had to come into the hospital. We were standing over the terrified patient, who was lying in the bed when the doctor leaned over the bed and pointed a finger in my face. "I told you—" I immediately interrupted him and said, "Do you want to do this in front of the patient?" The patient looked mortified, and the doctor decided to back off, at least for the moment.

He then placed a magnet over the pacemaker/defibrillator to shut it off, and the patient immediately went into cardiac arrest. We shocked the patient three times to resuscitate him. After stabilizing the patient, we left the room to write our notes of the event. I said to the doctor I was not impressed by his unprofessional behavior, and that I would be taking the matter up with hospital administration the next day. To his credit, he apologized and I think he did that so I wouldn't chart the actual events that occurred in the patient's record.

At least that patient's life was saved. That isn't always the case and it's sad when you lose someone in your family. Hopefully, you lose them after they have had many good years and a long life. It's always sad for a parent to lose a child and the grief can be overwhelming. It's especially difficult to lose a young vibrant new mother. Sadly, this occurred in the next example.

To those of you who may be on the fence about doing the research to find a good hospital and a good doctor, let me drive a point home from an experience I had while I was a hospital supervisor. After a new doctor came into a hospital group, I started to notice an increase in the number of patients coding in the hospital. As I documented my findings of the events that occurred during the codes, I kept seeing the same doctor's name. I quickly figured out in a two week period 80 percent of the patients that I was coding belonged to this one physician.

I was very concerned with my findings and scheduled a meeting with my manager. The manager found the data alarming and told me to continue to collect it, but at that time nothing was done about this doctor. Shortly after that conversation, this physician did a trans-esophageal echocardiogram (TEE) procedure on a young mother. She was having complications from childbirth, which landed her in the intensive care unit. A TEE procedure involves sedating the patient and placing a scope in their mouth and running it down the esophagus to examine the heart. The physician missed catching a dissecting aorta, which carries blood to various parts of your body after the blood leaves the heart. A dissecting aorta can cause blood to leak out of the artery and does occur sometimes with pregnancy. This young new mother coded in the ICU that evening. We all rushed in and did everything within our power to save her, but she died from a ruptured aorta despite our frantic efforts.

The patient's family, her husband, and the staff were utterly distraught over her death. Meanwhile, the physician and the head of that physician's department were present on the unit. The father of the deceased patient began to get irate, stating angrily, "I want to kick that doctor's ass." Everyone handles grief differently. The responsible physician did not have the intestinal fortitude to tell the family of the patient's death, so another doctor was handling the family and this tragic situation. Security was called, and I went to speak with the responsible physician. I spoke in a very professional manner, "The patient's father is extremely upset and wanted to—" and that is as far as I got. The responsible physician angrily said to me, "Of course he's very upset. His daughter just died. He has the right to be very upset." I replied, "Let me make this a little clearer for you. He wants to come out here and kick your ass, and as much as I would like to see that happen, I think it's time for you to leave the unit." The chair of the department added, "I think you should listen to him." I had worked with the chair of the department for years and I could tell by his tone that he was extremely upset.

Perhaps by now, you are wondering what happened to that

physician. Fortunately, he was no longer allowed to practice at the hospital. That was the straw that broke the camel's back. What I wrestle with is that he left a lot of patients and their family members in dire situations before anything was done to remove him from practice. We as patients and clinicians must change the system by holding those around us who lack good judgment and clinical skills accountable. Although I tried to do this, I feel I should have pushed harder and maybe that young mother would still be alive today. The payors, or the insurance companies, are starting to reimburse or provide payment according to patient outcomes, and that may help. This has got to change. If this were a bad auto mechanic, you would fire him after the first or second breakdown, right? This is not the first time and unfortunately will not be the last time someone became a victim of the American Healthcare System.

We have covered a lot of information in this chapter. The first was where to have your surgery. Remember, ambulatory surgical centers (ASC) usually cost less than having the surgery in the hospital. We discussed what questions to ask your surgeon once you have picked a quality surgeon. We discussed having a community hospital nurse in your network of friends, and I gave you some examples of things that went horribly wrong while I was working at a hospital. Being in control of your health care means being an active member of your health care team. Do your research, be an informed patient, and if you are having major surgery, have a loved one stay with you in the hospital, as hospitals get busy. Your loved one can look out for you so you can rest. All of these steps should make you knowledgeable and optimize your hospital experience.

NURSING KNOWLEDGE

Having a nurse in your network of friends and family is an invaluable resource. We care about our friends and family and can help you navigate the healthcare system to avoid unfortunate circumstances such as the examples in this chapter. Many times friends, family, and neighbors ask my wife and me for medical direction. If you don't know a nurse, ask your friends if they have one in their network. If they do meet with the nurse, buy them lunch in hopes to establish a relationship. It will be worth the cost of the meal. Connect with them on social media, as they will be a valuable resource.

CHAPTER 5

Make Your Wishes Known

....

Many people find it difficult to discuss end-of-life care. It is extremely important though, that you are prepared and have prepared your health care proxy for this care. Although difficult, all of us are going to die at some point and it can be an easy or difficult process depending on our circumstances and choices.

Here is a personal example of the difficulties involved. Although my mother and I had discussed a do not resuscitate (DNR) document and what it covered, she had never followed through on getting one. At the insistence of my sister, my mother brought it up to me and my wife while on a visit to our house. My stepfather whipped out his DNR, which he kept in his wallet, and said, "I have mine right here." She asked both of us what our opinion was.

I shared with her my nursing experience of coding people, the effects of doing cardiopulmonary resuscitation (CPR), and the experience of watching a breathing tube being inserted into someone's throat. I discussed with her how family members saw that patient after they had died. It is easy to break ribs during that procedure, there is quite a bit of bruising, and there can be trauma from the insertion of the breathing tube. I explained it is just not a good way for a family to have to view you if the intervention was not going to change the outcome anyway. A couple of months after that discussion my mother went back to her physician and asked for a do not resuscitate document, which she filled out and sent me a copy, as I was my mother's health care proxy.

Intentions Are Not Enough

At one point in my career, I worked with a doctor at a hospital in the emergency department. One night we had a patient come in and it was very apparent he was brain dead. Emergency medical services (EMS) coded this patient on the way in and although the body was functioning, he was not responding to any of the neuro checks used to see if the brain is functioning. The doctor looked up at me—I will never forget this moment—and said, "David, if that's me someday just pull the plug."

Several years later the same doctor coded in the men's locker room of the emergency department. It was a night I was not working and I still wrestle with that to this day. The outcome may not have been any different and I don't know how long he was unconscious before he received attention. Anyway, once stabilized he was transferred to an intensive care unit. He was there for quite a while. Medical tests revealed that he was brain dead. He was not the same guy that I knew.

His wife believed a miracle would occur and that he would one day wake up from his situation, so she allowed him to live that way. Even when staff and physicians talked to her about his wishes, she did not budge. Everyone handles grief differently and I believe she was in denial. She may not have been ready to lose him, and just being able to spend a few hours a day with him in a hospital room may have brought her some measure of comfort. I do not know what she was thinking, but I could still hear those words that he uttered to me in that emergency department "David, if that's me someday just pull the plug." I had no say in pulling the plug and I do not know how well he documented his last wishes.

He died a difficult death after spending 18 months in a long-term care facility with a trach, which is a tube in your neck to breathe through and being fed through a tube in his stomach. He came in and out of the hospital sometimes, with bedsores and various infections, until he finally passed. He did not have a good quality of life, so although the outcome did not change, the process for him could have been a lot different.

Be Clear About Your Wishes

It is especially important that you spell out with your health care proxy exactly what it is you want and do not want to be done in the form of an Advanced Directive. I have had to be a health care proxy for two of my family members and it was not easy, even though I am a nurse. Your health care proxy must be someone who will follow your wishes. I have seen situations in which family members have overridden the advanced directives. This went against what the patient wished for and took the time to document. That does happen, so you need to be aware of that when you choose your health care proxy. Plus, in having that discussion with your health care proxy, you take the tremendous burden away from them. It is extremely hard to make decisions in a crisis and having that discussion upfront helps that person make the correct decision for you.

My 84 year old mother called me one Friday extremely upset and said that she was on her way to the hospital because my stepfather had gotten into a motor vehicle accident and the police told her it was unbelievably bad. This was during the initial stage of the COVID-19 virus, so when they arrived, the hospital was not letting any visitors in. I called the unit where my stepfather was being cared for. They informed me that he had broken every one of his extremities, would require many surgeries and that he was on a ventilator.

I asked the nurse about my stepfather's DNR and they said they did not have a copy of it. I asked the nurse where my stepfather's wallet was and at first, they could not locate it. Later his wallet was located and his DNR was found inside. I was informed my stepfather might not make it through the night, so we developed a plan to take my mother to the hospital so she could see him. She saw him that Friday night with the help of some good friends.

My stepfather did make it through the night and had to go for multiple surgeries. They left the breathing tube in to keep him stable. Before the accident, he was going to take my mother to the emergency department because she was having chest pain. Knowing her cardiac situation, I knew there was nothing that they could do for her if she was having a heart attack.

During that weekend we talked to my mother quite a few times about my stepfather's condition. He had been through an accident like this many years ago when he was driving a truck and had said repeatedly he never would go through something like that again. During the course of those conversations, my mother kept saying, "I feel a great peace about all this," which caused my wife to turn and look at me with concern. My wife's experience in being a hospice nurse kicked in and she said she had heard this before from patients who were getting ready to die.

However, nothing could prepare me for the phone call that I got on Monday morning. A nurse from the emergency department called me and said we have your mother in our emergency department and she is having a heart attack. I knew this was not going to be a good outcome. They asked if they could put in a breathing tube and take her to the cardiac catheterization (cath) lab—and this is where it got dicey. My wife and I discussed it quickly and at first, we said yes. I tell you this because even with all my medical knowledge and experience, being her health care proxy and having to deal with it in a crisis, I caved in. I went into son mode. I could not take the thought of losing her, even though I knew there was nothing they could do for her in that cath lab.

This interfered with my following her wishes, even though we had this conversation many times. As a son, I found it hard to let go. I received a phone call about three minutes after the initial call. The emergency department nurse said her situation had changed and she was not a candidate to go to the cath lab. Although I knew that this meant my mother was dying, I was also relieved she was not going to be put on a ventilator. While the nurse was talking to me, she said she had just passed. A doctor was with my mother at the time, and I am sure he comforted her.

During a crisis when you must make split-second decisions about someone you love, it can be difficult to do the right thing. What was amazing is that my mother was not a highly organized individual, but she had her health care proxy, living will, and DNR paperwork with her. She came prepared and made sure the hospital knew of her wishes.

Multiple Decision Makers

Back to my stepfather. Although we had many discussions in which he desired to make me his health care proxy, unfortunately, he never followed through on that. So, there he was in the intensive care unit undergoing multiple surgeries and on a ventilator, which was something that he really did not want. The disconnect was that they did not find his DNR paperwork in his wallet when he arrived in the emergency department. In that case, you are legally bound to do everything possible to save that person.

Once my mother passed, his brother, with whom I had never interacted until this crisis, took over my stepfather's health care decisions, as he was his health care proxy. During this time I discussed with him that it would only be fair for my stepfather to know my mother had died. His brother was afraid that if he had that information, he would give up, so he decided to withhold it from him. When

I talked to the nursing staff, they told me that he was interactive, smiling, and was following commands. In fact, he was not even sedated which most people on ventilators are. The point is, he could have received that information, but at the hospital, they were instructed not to tell him. In fact, they were opening his get-well cards just in case there were bereavement cards in the stack.

I was in contact with his brother at least once a day during this time. He called me to tell me that a doctor had discussed with him that it was only fair that my stepfather knows that his wife had passed. They were trying to figure out how to tell him, as no visitors were allowed. My stepfather had a best friend that lived in the area that was willing to go to the hospital and tell him once they allowed visitation.

Meanwhile, when I talked to the nurses at the hospital they gave me information about his condition that didn't make sense to me. As we were learning more and more about the COVID-19 virus my wife and I both realized his symptoms matched many of the COVID-19 symptoms. We both thought somehow he had contracted it.

On the same day that the doctor was really pushing my stepfather's brother to tell him his wife had passed, my stepfather died, 12 days after my mother. I am not sure if the doctor told my stepfather my mother was gone and he gave up, or his heart just could not take it anymore, as he had a cardiac history. I do know that his life did not end the way he wanted it to.

Be Prepared

Although my stepfather was prepared, and we had many conversations about what should happen if he was incapacitated, he didn't follow through and get the correct paperwork for me to be his health care proxy. Although his wishes were known, they were not followed the way that he would have wanted them to be. So, my mom came in prepared with her paperwork, made her wishes known, and was able to go peacefully, while my stepfather was basically flogged before he died. He endured multiple surgeries, being put on dialysis, and being on a ventilator. The outcome was the same for both, but the dying process was very different.

The other thing to consider is given the COVID-19 virus, dying is vastly different and many patients have died alone like my stepfather. As a nurse, it is always hard to have those discussions with loved ones face to face and hold their hand while you comfort them, but now it has become less personal. Many doctors and nurses are calling loved ones and telling them their loved one is near death. Some of these loved ones live just blocks away from the hospital. They are unable to see the condition the patient is in, so that makes it much more difficult for them to receive the information that their loved one is dying. The loved ones are not able to be at the bedside, so there is no real closure. [6]

Since states vary on the paperwork you need, you will want to research the requirements for your state. The important take-away from this lesson is that we are all going to die at some time, so be very clear about what you want and do not want to be done when your time approaches. Have those conversations with your health care proxy, and make sure they have a copy of your paper-work. It is also important to choose someone who you know will follow your wishes. Your doctor, nurse, or social worker are a great resource for this information and can guide you in the cor-rect direction.

NURSING KNOWLEDGE

Have your paperwork in order and discuss your end of life wishes with your health care proxy. Considering who your health care proxy will be is extremely important as this person needs to understand your wishes and execute them. Having one of your children as your health care proxy can get complicated as many times they can't emotionally distance themselves in order to follow your wishes. This is one of the most important decisions you will ever make so think it through and make the best health care proxy choice that you can.

Part 2

Paying
for
Your
Care

CHAPTER 6

Why Your Prescriptions Cost So Much

The healthcare system is very complex. Navigating it as a patient can be difficult. While we have learned how to stay safe as a patient in the hospital in the first section, we are now going to learn how to handle these very profitable companies who are responsible for insuring you and setting the price points for your medications. We are going to shift our focus to costs associated with your health care so that you can understand what is happening behind the scenes.

Meet Sally, a diabetic patient who works as a Wal-Mart cashier. She is dependent upon life-saving shots of insulin to manage her blood sugar. Sally is also a single mother with three children: Alex, Heather, and Claude. Her ex-husband is serving a jail sentence for armed robbery, and therefore she receives no child support. One night after work she notices that Claude, her youngest, does not look good. He is hot, sweaty, coughing a lot, and complaining of pain in his right ear. She takes Claude's temperature and it is 104 degrees. She takes Claude to the emergency department (ED), and after a long wait, Claude is diagnosed with an ear infection. The ED doctor gives Sally a prescription for an antibiotic and gives Claude his first dose of the antibiotic.

Sally goes to the 24/7 pharmacy because it's now one o'clock in the morning. The pharmacist tells Sally her copay is 78 dollars. Sally is tired at this point and uses the money that she had put away to refill her insulin prescription, as she knows Claude needs this antibiotic.

In the morning, after getting Alex and Heather off to the bus stop so they can attend school, Sally checks her blood sugar. It is 182 and Sally would normally take four units of insulin to get it back to a normal level. Knowing that her insulin supply is running low and not having enough money to refill it, Sally decides to take two units.

Later in the week, Sally completely runs out of insulin. Knowing that she is getting paid in five days, Sally decides not to check her blood sugar and wait until she has enough money to refill her insulin. Sally tells her mother of her decision. Her mother is also struggling, as she is disabled and living on a fixed income. Three days later, her mother calls Sally's cell phone and doesn't get an answer. She takes the bus to Sally's apartment and finds her comatose, lying on the floor. The mother dials 911 and Sally is admitted to the hospital with a blood sugar of 821.

After her intensive care unit (ICU) stay the medical staff is able to regulate Sally's blood sugar back to normal limits and discharge her from the hospital. While in the hospital Sally talked with a social worker who was able to help her find a more affordable way to obtain her insulin, but Sally now has a large hospital bill that she will be responsible for. She returns home much more in debt than if she had proactively obtained her insulin and avoided a hospital stay.

Many Americans are living one crisis away from a health care emergency. How does this happen in one of the richest countries in the world? To understand that we will need to examine what goes on behind the cloaked practices of the pharmaceutical and insurance companies who continue to rake in mega profits.

Pharmaceutical companies take advantage of illness in our pill-driven society when people are at their most vulnerable. While many hospital systems run on margins or profits of one to three percent, the largest 25 pharmaceutical companies earn 15-20 percent profit. The sicker you are, the more likely the medicine you need to survive will cost more. Take for instance the high cost of cancer drugs.

People with cancer don't have a lot of options when they need medications, so the pharmaceutical companies inflate their prices.

Americans spent roughly $535 billion on prescription drugs in 2018. This is an increase of 50 percent as compared to what they spent in 2010. This far exceeds the cost of inflation, as big pharm increased prices on its most prescribed medications by 40 to 71 percent from the years 2011 to 2015. What this means is if you had a $200 prescription in 2011 and it shot up 50 percent in 2015 you would now be paying $300 for the same prescription. Meanwhile, most pay raises are approximately three percent a year meaning your pay from 2011 to 2015 on average would be 12 percent more. Your $200 prescription should only cost you $224, not $300 if it followed in line with your salary increases.

Pharmaceutical companies claim that they need to charge more for research and development, but they receive money from publicly funded research and tax breaks—in other words, your tax dollars. Since 1930 the National Institute of Health (NIH) has invested 900 billion dollars in research that formed the pharmaceutical and biotechnology sectors. Despite these investments, the typical US consumer pays more than other industrialized nations for their prescriptions. Maybe that's why so many Americans turn to Canada and Mexico to obtain their prescriptions. [7]

Let's look at a common example. A vial of life-sustaining insulin for type 1 diabetics retails at around $300 in the U.S. depending on your insurance plan. The price of insulin has doubled since 2012 and in the previous 10 years, it had nearly tripled. In total, insulin prices shot up 197 percent between 2002 and 2013. It's reported that 25 percent of people who need insulin report rationing it. This has led to needless harm and death. Recently, a 22 year old woman died due to insulin rationing. Like Sally, she was trying to save money by taking the bare minimum she needed. That cost-cutting measure cost her life.

NURSING KNOWLEDGE

If you are having a hard time paying for your prescriptions you have options. You can call your doctor's office and ask them to prescribe a lower-priced medication. You can also access your local or state agencies to see what solutions they offer. Your third option is to contact www.needymeds.org or call their toll-free helpline at 800-503-6897 to see if they can help you. Never stop taking a prescribed medication due to costs.

In 2019 the U.S. Senate Committee on Finance sent a letter to Eli Lilly inquiring the reason why the price of insulin was so high when the same vial of insulin costs $48 in Singapore, $14 in India, $6 in Austria, and $0 in Italy. That's a pretty significant cost saving compared to the United States, where it is produced.

The pharmacy companies also benefit from research and development tax credits. This credit was introduced in 1981 to encourage investment in pioneering research. The tax credit is available to companies that try to develop technologically improved products which some medications qualify for. On top of these tax credits pharmacy companies also receive a tax deduction for their marketing and advertising expenses. It must be pretty lucrative because in 1997 there were 79,000 ads for medications, including television commercials. That number exploded to 4.6 million in 2016. [7]

Once a drug is developed it can take 20 years or more before the brand name drug is released in generic form. A new drug is patented, which means only the drug maker can produce and sell the drug for 20 years from the filing date. Usually, these new drugs are priced high, as drug companies state they are hard to manufacture. If they are lifesaving drugs, they can virtually be unaffordable. Take, for instance, the drug Zolgensma, which is a miracle drug for children born with spinal muscular atrophy. It will only set you back $2.125 million per dose.

If the drug is profitable, the drug maker can change a chemical element and extend their patent to ensure even greater profits. Behind the scenes, there is a little known practice called "pay to delay" in which a brand name pharmaceutical firm strikes a deal with a generic drug company that prohibits competition between them. Studies have found that each year these anticompetition deals cost taxpayers and consumers over $3.5 billion in drug costs by not allowing new drugs to be offered in generic form.

Yet even in the area of generic drugs, you will find no relief. While generic drugs are supposed to save us money, Teva Pharmaceuticals, the largest generic drug supplier in the world, raised its prices 9 percent in 2019 and reported 18.8 million in revenue. Take, for example, the drug Daraprim, a drug used to treat infections common among people with AIDS. When the generic company producing this drug realized that no one else was producing a generic version, they hiked the price from $13.50 a pill to $750.

In 2018 the CEOs of three major pharmaceutical firms made $90 million, while Americans spent $535 billion on prescription drugs that same year. How does this play out? A 2019 report by the Centers for Disease Control and Prevention found that for adults under the age of 65, 11.4 percent report not taking their medications as prescribed to reduce health care costs. Many times those patients end up coming to the emergency department in crisis. Once stabilized, they are given prescriptions to fill at their local pharmacy. When they arrive they often find the co-pay for the medication is more than they can afford, so they do not fill the prescriptions. They then show up again in the emergency department in crisis, and the vicious cycle repeats itself.

Joe is an unemployed factory worker who suffers from high blood pressure. One evening he has a pounding headache and develops a nosebleed. He feels so bad that he goes to the emergency department (ED) to be seen. After taking his blood pressure, which is very high, the doctor at the ED medicates him with an antihypertensive drug and prescribes him Diovan to better control his high blood pressure. Joe then goes to fill his prescription at a local pharmacy. Since Joe has been unemployed for a year he has lost his employer-based insurance and is on Medicaid. The pharmacist tells Joe his medication is not covered by Medicaid, and he needs to pay $65 for the medication. Joe, not having the $65, leaves without the medication. Joe ends up in the emergency department one week later with the same symptoms.

A little-known fact: there is a law that prohibits Medicare from negotiating drug prices. So, the biggest payor or insurer in America is not allowed to negotiate drug prices by law. That makes no sense because if they could buy in bulk it would drive the prices down. Yet such a commonsense law would cut into the profit of those lobbyists lining the politicians' pockets. During the 2016 elections, the pharmaceutical industry spent $62 million to finance candidates, and they got what they paid for. In 2019 the Senate Finance Committee failed to pass an amendment on the Prescription Drug Pricing Reduction Act of 2019. This would have allowed Medicare to negotiate drug prices with manufacturers to drive down drug costs. [7] Just remember this when you have to pay an enormous cost for your next prescription. The people we are electing are not willing to take high drug prices on at the source.

Recently, some electronic medical records (EMRs) can price what the drug will cost the patient given their insurance, and the doctor can discuss it with the patient to see if it's affordable. This is a relatively new development and one that is sorely needed, as the majority of patients who return to the emergency department/ hospital are patients who didn't take their medications. One hospital that was seeing quite a few of these cases decided they would simply GIVE this patient population a 30 day supply of their medications before leaving the hospital. They found this strategy was more cost-effective and the patients got the treatment they needed.

Pharmacy Benefit Managers

Many people don't know what a pharmacy benefit manager is. I know I didn't until I started my doctorate and began to study what exactly are the factors that make medications so expensive. To get the full picture we must understand the history of this role. How did the pharmacy benefit manager role come to exist and what was the initial purpose?

In 1968 the role of the pharmacy benefit manager (PBM) was established with the first plastic benefit insurance card. By the 1970's they acted as intermediaries between insurance companies and pharmaceutical manufacturers by deciding prescription drug claims. In the 1980s they moved from doing this via paper to doing it electronically. In the 80's the PBM role became a major player as health care and prescription costs were increasing. Originally the pharmacy benefit manager's role was to recommend lower priced generic drugs to doctors to aid in keeping costs down. That changed quietly in 2007 when CVS acquired Caremark a PBM firm. The role changed from the processing of prescription transactions to managing the pharmacy benefit for health plans or insurers. By 2015 there were approximately seven lawsuits or antitrust claims stating that pharmacy benefit managers had defrauded and deceived insurance companies. In 2017 the *Los Angeles Times* wrote an article on how the pharmacy benefit manager role caused an increase in drug costs, especially in the area of diabetes (remember that $300 vial of life saving insulin)? Clearly, the model had changed and not for the better. [8]

PBMs are probably handling your prescription costs and you may not even know it. If you use Express Scripts, CVS Health, or OptumRX, which process 70 percent of claim volumes—and this is not an exhaustive list—your insurance company is using a PBM. This role primarily negotiates the price of medications between drug manufacturers and pharmacies while looking out for the insurance company. Initially, they were supposed to be looking out for the costs for the patient, but with any business model that runs behind the scenes secretively, corruption can factor in. If you don't believe me, try to call your insurance company the next time you run into a high-priced prescription and ask to speak to the PBM who negotiated the price. Just make sure you have a few hours to kill because I do not know of one person who has ever directly spoken to a pharmacy benefit manager.

The Pharmacy Benefit Manager Role

A PBM sits in the middle of the distribution chain for your prescription drugs. They maintain drug formularies or lists of covered medications by the health insurers. This influences the medications you can use and also the out of pocket expenses for those medications. They use their purchasing power to negotiate discounts and rebates from drug manufacturers, which in the past they were supposed to pass on to the patient or insurance company. Sounds simple enough, right? Except the PBMs receive a much larger rebate for more expensive drugs than they do for drugs that may provide better value at lower costs. This results in higher out of pocket costs for the patient. If you are being treated for high blood pressure and your doctor prescribes you the brand name drug Lopressor and checks the box allowing you to be prescribed the generic version metoprolol, it will be the PBM who will decide what drug they fill the prescription with. Many times that decision is based on the rebate the PBM will receive.

NURSING KNOWLEDGE

A quick way to tell if you have a brand name drug or a generic drug is by looking at the drug name. If it starts with a capital letter it's a brand name drug. If it starts with a lowercase letter it's a generic drug.

Even the drug manufacturers argue the increasing rebates (which they control) and what they pay the PBMs are forcing them to increase their drug prices. Big pharms rebates to the PBM's increased from 39.7 billion in 2012 to 89.5 billion in 2016. There is a great debate over whether the PBM's should be able to keep the rebates they receive from drug manufacturers. Some suggest that these savings should be passed to insurers and payors to bring down the insurance premiums we consumers pay. The PBMs often pocket the rebates they receive as this business practice is shrouded in secrecy and there is no real accountability.

Another controversy is a practice that the PBMs use called "spreading pricing." This occurs when the PBM is reimbursed by health plans for a higher price than the PBM pays the pharmacies for the drugs. The PBM usually keeps the difference. So why is this practice allowed to happen? It all has to do with the lack of transparency. The payments the PBMs generate for pharmacies are kept confidential from health plans as well as the government. Health care seems to be riddled with the lack of transparency especially in the payment models. [9]

How does this play out in medical care? I know of an oncologist who was treating a stage 4 (worst possible stage for cancer) patient who was prescribed a chemotherapeutic drug they felt would work with the patient's other underlying chronic conditions. The drug the doctor prescribed was rejected by the insurance company because the PBM felt the doctor could first try a lower cost option. Now, someone with stage 4 cancer doesn't have a lot of time to mess with lower cost cancer medications. When the doctor pressed the issue, the insurance company stood its ground. When the doctor pressed them to speak to the PBM, the insurance company told the doctor this was not possible. Here we have a decision maker (the PBM) who is inaccessible but allowed to direct medical care? Those of us in the medical community are astounded that the insurer and PBM role have this much power over patients.

The Disruptors

My female dog Pippi Lou took Viagra. That's because Viagra was originally invented to reduce pulmonary hypertension. Only later was it discovered that Viagra had the side effect of alleviating erectile dysfunction. In any case, when the vet first prescribed the medication, my wife priced it at over $700 for a one month supply! I love my dog, but that seemed a little unreasonable.

My wife turned to the internet to figure out a lower-cost alternative. She found the GoodRx app and downloaded it to her smartphone. Using the GoodRx app, she was able to find it at $63 for a one month supply from another retailer. That's a savings of 91 percent. Mind you, we were not using an insurance company or going through a pharmacy benefit manager. We were just trying to give our older dog a good quality of life. So how did GoodRx shave 91 percent off the price of the Viagra prescription?

As we have learned, drug prices are anything but transparent. In fact, the pharmaceutical companies try to keep them as secret as possible citing these prices are trade secrets. Most consumers do not know what their prescription will cost until they get to the pharmacy. Maybe that's why 200 million filled prescriptions are left at the counter every year. [10]

Most people are not aware that the price depends on the pharmacy you use. You could have a prescription that costs $450 at CVS and may cost you $250 at Walgreens. What other industry operates in secrecy like this? Could you imagine picking up a loaf of bread without a price tag and then getting to the checkout register to find out it costs you $20?

GoodRx realized this when one of the cofounders tried to fill a prescription only to realize the price of the prescription varied greatly between pharmacies. This led them to create a free app that could price prescriptions near your home or work. They do this by partnering with pharmacy chains such as Walmart, CVS, Walgreens, Target, etc., and believe it or not, pharmacy benefit managers as well as pharmaceutical companies. This endeavor has led to real-time pricing at over 70,000 locations nationwide. The company claims to have helped Americans save 10 billion dollars since they launched the app in 2011. This is critical as the 20 most commonly prescribed brand name drugs for seniors have risen 10 times more than the annual rate of inflation according to a congressional report released in 2019. [10] GoodRx claims that they helped 18 million customers who couldn't afford their prescriptions without the use of their platform. GoodRx also had 4.4 million monthly active consumers and 15 million visitors during the second quarter of 2020. GoodRx reports that they are the largest platform out there for gathering prescription drug prices. [11]

GoodRx works by easily allowing you to look up the name of your medication and showing you coupons from manufacturers, pharmacies, and even GoodRx. You can find the lowest price on GoodRx, then check with the pharmacy to discover what the medication would cost you using your insurance, and then using this information you can pick from the lower priced option. Many times it's the GoodRx price, which makes you wonder why you are paying so much for an insurance plan when a free app can help you save more on your prescription costs. One thing to note is if you are paying a high out-of-pocket deductible, save your receipts as your GoodRx prescription will not be applied to your deductible at the pharmacy. Instead, it will be listed as a cash sale, meaning your insurance will never know you purchased it at that pharmacy. You can take your receipts and see if your insurance company will allow you to apply them to your deductible, but that is up to your insurance company. While there are other companies out there that can offer prescription drug price relief, GoodRx is certainly one of the first innovators in this arena. [10]

Other disruptors in the prescription world include ride-share companies like Uber and Lyft. Both companies are partnering with health care organizations to make sure you have rides to and from your health care appointments. They are also getting into prescription delivery services. Uber has partnered with NimbleRx, which is an on-demand prescription platform that can be accessed by an app. You can even set the date and time for your prescription deliveries. NimbleRx is another startup company that wants a piece of the 3.5 trillion dollar health care market by offering home delivery of your prescription medications. NimbleRx already has 500 million dollars in annual revenue and usually partners with drugstore chains that have at least 10-20 stores. Their partnership with Uber should help them expand into the market significantly. [12]

This type of model makes sense with Amazon, who recently purchased an online pharmacy PillPack, which breaks your prescriptions down into daily doses and ships them to consumers. The health care community recognizes that adherence to prescription medications can keep people out of the hospital and improve their overall quality of life. With the pandemic keeping seniors at home safely, has become a priority. Using alternative methods to deliver prescription medications has taken off and companies like Amazon's PillPack, NimbleRx, and Uber are on the cutting edge. I am sure we will see more disruptors emerge in the marketplace.

Chapter 7

The Labyrinth of Insurance

Insurance companies serve as the middlemen between you and the health care organizations, doctor's office, and pharmacies with whom you choose to do business. Before the Affordable Care Act (ACA) America's healthcare system ranked last in affordability and patient access in the world. More people in America were denied benefits based on preexisting conditions for things such as cancer, pregnancy, asthma, and high blood pressure. [13] Can you imagine the advantage of having a business in which you could provide services to people who really didn't need them but refuse services, or not take on any risk, for people who did require services?

Insurance companies make money by taking in revenue and finding ways not to pay for health care. [14] Just ask anyone who has wrestled with attempting to get reimbursed by their insurance company. The longer the insurance company can avoid reimbursing you, the more interest they are making on your money. They hope that you will get frustrated and stop submitting your claim so they can keep the profit. Just like the pharmaceutical companies, they are beholden to their shareholders, as they are a business and not really in the "caring for others" mindset that your nurse or doctor is. Insurance companies or payors as we call them in the medical community, understand that health care reimbursement is complex and they do nothing to ease the burden of the layman who has to deal with them. In fact, they actually have protocols that make it more complex for you to be reimbursed.

I had a dear sweet aunt of mine pass away from cancer. My aunt had no children and I was the son she never had. When she finally passed away she left me the job of settling her estate. Most of it was pretty straightforward until I had to settle some insurance claims. My aunt's insurance company began denying reimbursement for intravenous (IV) supplies that she had needed to be treated for her illness. It was a significant amount of money and I attempted to work with them. I was able to locate the doctor's orders for the supplies from the home care agency that had cared for my aunt. I submitted them to the insurance company and heard nothing back from them for over two weeks. When I called to inquire, I was told that the person who handled this type of claim was on vacation and to try back the following week, which I did.

It took this person another week before they returned my call, at which point I was told that they didn't cover IV supplies for the type of intravenous procedure my aunt had needed. Being a nurse, I stated that in order to do an intravenous procedure, you need IV supplies and this was not an acceptable answer. I asked to speak to a supervisor and was routed to phone call hell, waited over 45 minutes for a supervisor, and was subsequently disconnected.

It was becoming apparent I was not going to reach someone who could settle my aunt's estate's insurance claim. The insurance company was using the oldest trick in the book and was banking on me getting so frustrated with them that I would give up. I began to explore other ways to settle this claim.

One of my friends who is a medical doctor suggested I call her elected official's office and explain the situation, as they had been able to help a patient of theirs in the past. Since I was desperate and willing to try anything at this point, I called my aunt's federal Senator's office. Much to my surprise I was placed on a brief hold and connected with an aide for the Senator. When I explained what was going on, the aide said they have had problems with this insurance company in the past. They had someone who could address this by the end of the week. Within three days I had a call from the insurance company stating the expenses would be covered in full. Within a week I had a check for the full reimbursed amount.

Why did I have to appeal to a Senator's office to resolve the claim? You won't find that move in any of the handbooks, except this one. If you are having this kind of experience while trying to process a claim, remember that these elected officials do work for you.

While reimbursement is one thing, insurance companies have also been known to actively intervene/interfere with a member's care, as the example below shows.

While my wife was working as a hospice home care nurse she had a patient who had insurance from a company that is widely advertised. This patient was on end of life care, and her job was to make this patient's last days as comfortable as possible. After talking with the patient and their family, my wife learned that when the patient was first diagnosed with cancer, the patient was prescribed chemotherapy, which would have allowed her a fighting chance—only to be denied the treatment by her insurance company because the cost was too high. It was more cost advantageous to the insurance company to place this patient on end of life care to manage their symptoms instead of paying for expensive chemo drugs. The patient's insurance company even refused to cover the cost of pain medications essential to keeping this patient comfortable.

Insurance companies get away with this stuff all of the time. The medical community can get so frustrated with the payors (insurance companies) because they do not make it easy to collect reimbursement. The insurance company decided that to save costs, this patient would be denied a chance at life.

NURSING KNOWLEDGE

If an insurance company is refusing to pay for your care, read your policy to become educated on their reason for denial. Call your doctor's office/hospital to make sure the claim was properly submitted. You can also check with your state insurance department. If all else fails, you can appeal the claim denial, because many times these are settled in the patient's favor. You can also contact your local news media, as insurance companies hate negative publicity and often times quickly settle. Do not take no as an answer!

The Fix

Insurance companies are essentially middlemen. In a disruptive model which is occurring more and more often, companies choose to self-insure. During the implementation of Obamacare, I had the luxury to work at such a company. We were rewarded for staying at a healthy weight, getting proactive care such as drug therapy for high cholesterol, and increasing our activity. While the rest of America was hit with very high insurance premiums, the company that I worked for was rewarding us for good behaviors and actually decreasing the amount of money they paid for our health care.

This is a new concept for many Americans. The choices that I was making, such as choosing to eat a burger or a salad at lunch and whether to be inactive all day or to walk 10,000 steps a day, was lowering the amount of money that I was paying toward my insurance premium. If you were obese or had poor health, you paid more than the person maintaining a healthy lifestyle. If you have a chance to work for a company that self-insures and removes the insurance middleman, you will undoubtedly pay less for your insurance.

Many in health care believe that insurance companies have too much power. If patients were allowed to pick the doctors and hospitals that they wanted, they would have better outcomes. The problem is the patients are not the ones paying. What you have is a model in which the insurance company that is paying are trying to decrease the bottom line while the patient who isn't paying has to play by their rules. [14] The insurance companies don't want you to know about companies that self-insure because that will put them out of business.

What Happens to My Insurance Premium Dollars?

About 30 percent of every dollar you spend goes to the administrative branch of health care. That's a whopping 30 cents on every dollar. That's roughly $569 billion a year. Much of this amount goes to billing and insurance related costs. The evidence shows that the American Healthcare System is spending about twice as much on administrative costs as other country providing world class health care. [15] For example, Duke University's hospital system has 957 beds and nearly 1,600 billing clerks. In Canada, which has a one-payor system, a hospital of this size typically has a handful of billing clerks. That's because there are so many different payors in the American Healthcare System, meaning there are many different billing and reimbursement practices depending on the payor.

An additional cost goes to overhead. In the insurance business, 80 percent of every insurance dollar is considered the Medical Loss Ratio (MLR). This means the insurance companies "lose" this money to the hospitals, providers, and other entities that cover health care. The Affordable Care Act (ACA) has a mandate that larger insurance companies have to spend 85 percent and smaller insurance companies 80 percent on health care, leaving 15 to 20 percent left for the insurance companies to keep. Before this ACA mandate insurance companies only had to have a medical loss ratio of 55 to 65 percent. [16]

Part of that 15-20 percent cut of your health care dollars goes toward the Chief Executive Officers' (CEOs) salaries. For example, United Healthcare Group's CEO made $18.1 million in 2018. This is 316 times the companies median employee salary, and with stock and stock options his salary was boosted to $21.5 million. All combined, the CEOs of eight of the largest publicly traded insurance companies made $143.5 million in total compensation in 2018, up 14.4 percent. These companies recorded a combined $21.9 billion in profits in 2018 on revenue of $718 billion. [17]

My wife in one of her home care positions had the mother of a Chief Financial Officer (CFO) for a larger well known insurance company as a patient. The wife of this CFO didn't want the mother living with them when she became ill, so the CFO had a wing built onto his house to accommodate the needs of his mother. He hired private duty nurses to care for his mother 24 hours a day 7 days a week. His teenage children both drove new BMWs and had manicures and pedicures weekly, and wore designer clothes. She would remark that she saw many patients during her week on home visits but nothing as elaborate as how this patient was taken care of. I have no issue with people succeeding and having a nice lifestyle but having dealt with an insurance company for my aunt's estate and knowing how hard they worked to attempt to deny her estate reimbursement, I couldn't help but wonder how much of the CFO's income could be due to the bad practices of his company.

The Problem with Medicare for All

The enormous salaries of these insurance company executives did not go unnoticed. During the 2020 presidential primaries, Senator Bernie Sanders pointed to this excess as a good reason to promote Medicare for all as a universal payment system. He cited that we could wipe out all these third-party payors to simplify and drive down costs. What he failed to mention is that Medicare only pays 80 percent reimbursement to hospitals and doctors. The healthcare system relies on third-party insurers or individual patients paying out of pocket to make up this gap. At the same time, many hospitals run on a one to three percent profit margin. Anyone who understands basic math understands that those numbers don't add up. Rural hospitals would not be able to continue to operate under this model. Many people would be denied health care under a Medicare for all model due to small hospitals failing to be reimbursed adequately and closing their doors.

Options for Continued Insurance Coverage While Unemployed

Since so many people in America depend on an employer for health care insurance, losing your job becomes very problematic. According to a federal law named Consolidated Omnibus Budget Reconciliation Act of 1985 (COBRA) employees of companies who employ 20 people or greater have up to 60 days to extend their health care insurance coverage after a job termination. Be warned that you will have to pay all days in the coverage period. If you were laid off in May and elect to use your COBRA benefits in July you would need to pay the premiums from the date you were laid off in May until the date you decide to sign up for COBRA. A good reason to elect COBRA is if you have already paid your out-of-pocket expense for the year or your deductible you wouldn't have to pay it twice as your COBRA insurance is simply a continuation of your current employer based plan. Some state laws cover people employed by companies with less than 20 people, but all of them are costly and require the employee to pay their usual premium as well as what the employer would pay, making them much too costly for people living from paycheck to paycheck. Still, if you did have a medical emergency within the first 60 days of losing your job, it would be worth enrolling in a COBRA plan. [18]

This shift in lost benefits means greater use of benefits such as Medicaid. Enrollment for Medicaid has grown to 4.3 million people since February 2020 and could grow even more. Medicaid is one of the biggest safety net programs in the United States, providing health care insurance to some 66.8 million Americans, or 20 percent of the nation's population. During COVID-19, the Medicaid rolls have grown even further, taxing the states to deal with the financial fallout with limited federal support. [18]

If you have lost your employer based health care insurance, you have several options. The first option is if you have a spouse or partner who has health care insurance you could be added to their policy, as the loss of a job qualifies as a life-changing event. If you are under 26 years old you can be added to your parents' insurance. These are the two easiest options you can exercise.

If these options are not viable alternatives for you, other options include COBRA which we mentioned previously, Medicaid (if you qualify), or buying insurance through an Affordable Care Act (ACA) insurance exchange. You can also buy a policy directly from an insurance provider but make sure it's an ACA policy. As the recent pandemic has shown, going without insurance is not a good idea.

One of the first things that you should do if you lose your employer sponsored health care insurance benefits is check to see if you are eligible for Medicaid. It is a state and federally run program that provides health care insurance at little to no cost to its recipients. The recipients must meet a certain income threshold, and while many states have expanded Medicaid coverage, some states have not. Your eligibility to enroll will be dependent on which state you live in. Medicaid is your easiest and lowest cost alternative to obtaining health care insurance.

A low-cost option for covering your children is the Children's Healthcare Insurance Program or CHIP. It has different requirements from state to state but is usually more generous in its income allowance. To be eligible for Medicaid you can make up to 138 percent of the federal poverty line in some states for 2020, which is $12,760 for an individual and $26,200 for a family of four. With CHIP in some states, you can make more than 400 percent of the federal poverty line and still be eligible. You will at least be able to get your children covered.

If Medicaid, CHIP, and COBRA don't meet your needs, you may be eligible to buy an insurance plan through the Affordable Care Act marketplace. After losing a job, you will be eligible for a special enrollment of 60 days prior to your job loss or after your job loss to enroll. For most states, you can find the information at healthcare. gov, although a handful of states and Washington DC run their own exchanges and require you to buy your health care plan there. People who make up to 400 percent of the federal poverty level may qualify. People making middle class wages are eligible for subsidiaries. The ACA subsidiaries are effectively tax credits that they give to you in advance. Even if your income shifts and you obtain another job, you will just have to pay back anything you underestimated when filing your federal taxes without any tax penalty. With COBRA, Medicaid, or an ACA health care exchange plan you can cancel the insurance at any time if you obtain another job.

The last option is buying an insurance plan outright. This can be a little complicated because insurance brokers will offer you low cost plans that may have some stipulations regarding preexisting conditions—not covering what an ACA health care exchange plan would. In other words, if something looks too good to be true it usually is. As a consumer, you can ask the insurance agent if this is an Affordable Care Act approved marketplace insurance plan. [19]

If your income drops to 400 percent of the federal poverty line, you will not be able to collect any subsidiaries if you have not purchased a plan through the ACA health care exchange. This is a factor you need to be aware of if you feel your financial situation is going to change.

How to Handle Big Medical Bills Without Insurance

Suppose you let your insurance lapse or didn't make the decision to continue it within the allotted time frame. You do have some alternatives when it comes to handling medical bills— what the industry calls a private pay individual. You will have to pay your bills, but there are ways that you can go about doing that without affecting your credit scores.

The first thing you should do is look at your bill. I know this sounds like a no-brainer, but hospitals quite often make billing mistakes. If you were discharged in the morning, they may charge you a full day hospital rate. They possibly could charge you for medications that you've never taken or procedures that were never performed. It's very important that you look at your bill and determine the validity of the charges that are on it.

Equally important, you should not ignore your bill. One way or the other, you will have to pay this money back. But if you choose to ignore it, your credit rating is going to take a hit as they will send your bill to a bill collector. This will cost you a lot of money if you ever anticipate taking out a loan for a car or a mortgage on a house. A bill collector gets paid a certain percentage on the amount they can collect from you. In my experience, most bill collectors are pretty ruthless in trying to extract money from you. At all costs, you want to avoid that headache. Get in front of this instead of letting the situation manage you and you'll do yourself a huge favor.

Develop a Payment Strategy

You can contact the hospital and work out an interest free payment plan. Usually, information within your bill discusses that option, but it's often in the fine print. Now when you do this a hospital is going to ask you for an amount that you probably cannot afford as a monthly payment. Do not be afraid to negotiate this amount. Talk to them about your extenuating circumstances. Ultimately you're trying to reach a price that both you and the hospital find affordable. If you try to stretch yourself too thin and can't make the payments, you're right back in the same boat, so again explain your circumstances and try to find a figure that you both find acceptable.

The worst thing you can do is take out a loan or put the balance on a credit card, as you will pay a lot more interest if you use either of these options. Keep in mind that the hospital wants to settle this as quickly as possible, and they will probably suggest a loan or a credit card as a viable alternative. Again, you do not want to use this method to pay your medical bills so continue to negotiate between yourself and the hospital arriving at a figure that you can both live with.

If you're fortunate enough to be able to pay the entire bill off in 30-90 days, you can ask for a prompt pay discount. Hospitals negotiate different figures for different insurance companies based on the procedures that you're having done at their hospital. You can use the same negotiating technique when you're acting as a private pay individual. Most often you will get hit with the full price of your hospital stay and any procedures because an insurance company covers multiple people, thus allowing them to negotiate the price down. Lucky for you, there are some online resources that list the fair price to pay for a medical procedure in your area. One of those tools is called the healthcare blue book. Here is the link: https://www.healthcarebluebook.com/ui/consumerfront

The free version of this tool allows you to enter your zip code and shows you an acceptable payment for various procedures. This will give you a starting point in negotiating a prompt pay discount with the hospital. If you're being billed toward the high end of a procedure, you should be able to negotiate it down toward the lower end.

If you fit the hospital's criteria, you can also apply for financial assistance. Do know that you will have to provide the hospital with quite a bit of paperwork, including your tax returns, pay slips, bank statements, current debt, and anything else that they may require to use this benefit. Many hospitals will make you apply for Medicaid first, which will lengthen the process.

Negotiations get harder once a collection agency is involved, so get in front of this. You want to offer to pay them something, as that is a show of good faith. If you negotiate properly, the figure should be what you can afford as well as income that the hospital can count on. Most hospitals have two sides to the business. On one side is the caring of the patient by the clinicians, and the other side is the business office, which has to bring in income for the health care organization to survive.

Working with your hospital on a payment strategy is important, but if you feel that you can't get any further with the individual that you're talking to, do not be afraid to ask to speak to their boss or another individual. Like any other profession, some people are very good at what they do and want to meet your needs because you are a paying customer of the hospital. Other individuals may not like their jobs and sometimes don't act very happy during the negotiation process. It is your right to deal with someone in the business office who is sensitive to your needs. You are respecting the fact that the hospital needs to make money to provide care for your community, and the hospital respects that health care can be very costly and works with their community members to ensure a payment plan meets their needs as well as the hospitals. [20]

NURSING KNOWLEDGE

Never take out a loan or use a credit card to pay off a hospital bill. Work with the hospital to develop a payment plan and save yourself many dollars in interest. Negotiation is the key.

CHAPTER 8

Skin in the Game

The current payment structure for a hospital, doctor's office, or any other health care entity is based on fee-for-service. This means that when you get sick, the hospital or other entity will bill your insurance company, Medicare, or Medicaid by using codes to describe your diagnosis and treatment plan. They will then be reimbursed accordingly, and you will end up paying what's leftover once you have met your deductible. It's important that you get a global view of the payment structure to understand the changes that are coming to health care because the payment structure and how you will receive health care are changing.

Think about my emergency department (ED) visit. I went to the ED because I was sick. There was no initial discussion about how much the visit would cost when I arrived, as I needed health care, and not receiving this care could have been detrimental to my health. That's the differentiator between health care and other businesses. If you are driving an old car and you need a new car, you visit a dealership, negotiate the price and decide whether you're going to continue to drive that old car or buy a new car. In health care you're not given that option, you're usually faced with a situation in which you need health care and you need it quickly. Because of that, the billing of health care is significantly different from the buying of goods.

After my emergency department visit I was billed not once but three times for different services. I received a bill from the hospital, physician practice, and the radiology department. On all three of the bills I received, my insurance information was inaccurate. At registration, I had offered to let them make a copy of my insurance card, but they said I was in the system and they had my insurance information. Six long months after my emergency department visit, only two of my three bills had been paid. The third bill from the hospital was not paid because they had not been able to get my group ID number correct on my insurance plan. This has cost me multiple phone calls with time spent on hold trying to rectify it. In fact, my bill went to a bill collector eventually, even though the hospital told me to disregard the notices I was receiving while they worked on the claim. It was only after I provided the bill collection firm a copy of the claim from my insurance company showing them the entire balance was paid off seven months earlier that the claim was settled.

Now if I were buying goods, I would just simply say I'm not going to deal with that company anymore, correct? I would say that's too much of a hassle and I would find a company that treated me better. In health care that's not an option. Usually, you don't have two or three different hospitals in the same city, and even if you did, chances are you would have a similar experience at all of the hospitals.

Compare that to your doctor's office. When I do my wellness visits yearly they bill my insurance company directly and that process works. It's different because I could fire my doctor and find another doctor if I were dissatisfied with the way I was being treated or the way I was being billed. I can't fire my local hospital because if I get sick again, I will need to go there.

If you have been diagnosed with congestive heart failure (CHF) and were admitted to the hospital in a CHF crisis, meaning you had symptoms such as shortness of breath, fatigue, and fluid buildup in your legs, it now becomes the care team's responsibility to keep you well enough that you will not be readmitted within the next 30 days upon discharge. This is a regulatory standard. In the past, if your condition was not managed correctly, the doctor and the hospital would collect additional revenue if you were readmitted in a week. Now that the doctor and hospital are accountable for keeping you out of the hospital for at least 30 days, they have to think about the long-term management of your care and not just the episode or crisis that caused you to be admitted. These shifts in the payment model are causing the providers of care such as the doctors and the hospitals to shift their mindset.

Reducing the Costs by Housing the Homeless

With health care costs increasing faster than inflation, the payors recognize that we need to move to a different model to drive down costs. Where you get your care also is a cost factor. If you're going to a doctor's office, you're probably going to pay less than if you show up in the emergency department. Using the emergency department for primary care can be very costly. The real bottom line here is if the community can stay healthy, the cost of health care should go down. Let's look at an example of how United Healthcare, one of the largest insurance companies in the country, got creative to reduce health care associated costs.

Back in 1986 the Emergency Medical Treatment and Active Labor Act (EMTALA) was enacted. This law barred hospitals that participated in federal health programs from turning away anyone unable to pay for health care. This act requires hospitals to evaluate and stabilize any patients who come to the emergency department. This allows the homeless a last-ditch refuge.

More than half a million homeless people are living in America. About one-third of them are living on the streets while others are living in shelters or with other individuals. When this population needs medical care or simply a meal and warm shelter, they end up in the nation's emergency departments. This is not a cost effective model, as oftentimes it would be cheaper to house these individuals than to continue to pay (or write off) their emergency department visits.

Many states use companies like United Healthcare to manage their Medicaid programs, as setting up a program with limited reimbursement can be difficult. Medicaid pays about 30 percent less than Medicare and covers much of the homeless population. Usually, the insurer gets a per-head member fee of anywhere between 500 to 1,000 dollars monthly. United Healthcare, which manages the Medicaid population in parts of Arizona, quickly examined the spending of some of their highest-cost Medicaid patients to reduce costs. One patient in particular whose illnesses included multiple sclerosis, diabetes, heart disease, and cerebral palsy was homeless and costing the insurer on average $12,945 a month for emergency department visits and inpatient stays. Once the insurer was able to provide adequate housing and a health care coach their monthly costs averaged $2,073 a month. This is a savings of more than 80 percent a month!

Our current healthcare pay-for-fee service is not set up to take care of homeless individuals. Most of the reimbursement is spent when people get sick and have to use the healthcare system via normal channels such as clinics or hospitals. Little money is spent managing the homeless population to keep them healthy.

It's important to note that Americans spend 18 percent of the gross national product (GDP) on health care while only spending 60 cents per dollar on social support. Other industrialized nations spend about 8.6 percent of their GDP on health care and 2 dollars per every health care dollar on social support. I find this interesting as the United States is the only country that turns to a for-profit entity such as United Healthcare by paying them taxpayer dollars to manage the homeless or poorer populations. This gives insurance companies influence in health care only secondary to the government which is the largest health care payor. United Healthcare insures 43 million people nationwide and owns Optum (remember our pharmacy benefit managers) as well as pharmacies and even Brazilian hospitals. Their shareholders expect growth of 13 to 16 percent annually. No wonder they place such emphasis on decreasing the costs of their Medicaid managed population.

United Healthcare bought an apartment complex in Maryvale, Arizona, which is a downtrodden neighborhood in Phoenix. The company spends about $1,200 to $1,800 to house these homeless individuals monthly. The individuals are encouraged to apply for disability to offset their day-to-day expenses. The business model calls for seeking homeless individuals who spend greater than $50,000 a year in medical expenses, mostly from the emergency department and inpatient stays. Other homeless individuals who may need a home just as much and do not meet the spending requirements are not eligible for the program, as it doesn't pay for United Healthcare to provide them with a home. They are also looking for individuals who want the help and will comply with the program, thus bringing their health care expenses down. Individuals who continue to go to the emergency department and do not decrease health care costs usually find themselves back on the streets.

What looks like a very humanitarian program to house homeless people is really an out-of-the-box business model meant to drive down costs and return profits to their shareholders. Granted, homeless housing does help some people, but only the right mix of them. The individual has to want the help and comply with the program rules to reap the benefits. What the government couldn't accomplish, the insurance companies who go at risk could figure out. Going at risk means the insurance company gets a certain amount of money a month. This is called capitation. In this case, it was between $500 to $1,000 per head. Anything they spend over that they have to take as a loss, but if they spend less they get to keep the difference as profit. Remember GoodRx our prescription disrupter? Both of these companies are doing something that the government can't seem to accomplish. They are driving down health care costs. Please note, though, that they are doing this with an emphasis on personal accountability and keeping people out of the emergency room/hospitals or reducing the costs of their high priced medications. This is going to be important as we discuss the new model of care delivery called Value-Based Care in Part 3 of the book. [21]

Price Transparency in Healthcare

While researching information for this book I came across a story in which a double lung transplant patient received a shocking health care bill. This gentleman was on an organ transplant list, and while waiting for the transplant he stopped breathing at his home. His wife called 911 and he was transported to their local hospital and admitted to the Intensive Care Unit (ICU). While there he almost died, but miraculously a set of donor's lungs that were a perfect match for him became available. He was then transported via helicopter to a major teaching hospital where the surgery was performed.

When this man received his bill he was charged $40,575 for the surgery, which included a charge of $31,605 for his surgeon. The real surprise is the helicopter company, which was outside of his network, charged him $51,282 to transport him. This was more money than the surgery itself. This is called surprise billing, and it occurs when an entity is outside of your insurance companies network. In this case, a law in 1978 called the Federal Airline Deregulation Act prohibits states from enacting price laws on air carriers, which could have made this helicopter company in network, thus reducing the costs.

Can you imagine the stress of recovering from a double lung transplant and getting socked with a surprise bill like that? Plus, the helicopter company was relentless in its pursuit of the money. They even called this man's daughter, asking her how they were going to pay the bill. The bill was eventually settled after *Good Morning America* picked up his story. This poor gentleman couldn't shop for his health care as his situation was an emergency. [22]

NURSING KNOWLEDGE

The use of media in a situation in which you have been wronged by a healthcare entity is extremely powerful. Healthcare entities do not want any negative publicity and will usually stop their pursuit if called out publicly.

Price transparency in health care in its current state was basically nonexistent until January 2021 when hospitals were required to list the costs for some procedures or face daily fines. Although some electronic medical records (EMR's) vendors are adding prescription copay amounts at the time the doctor is prescribing the prescription, a lot more work needs to be done. Health care insurance companies and pharmaceutical companies have an elaborate system to dodge and weave price transparency or what you will end up paying for your health care.

A friend of mine had to have an MRI. She was charged $1,750 for the test. Yet she said she knew someone else who had the exact same test done with the exact same health care organization and was charged a co-pay of $50. She couldn't understand why that happened. I explain to her that insurance companies barter with different health care organizations to reduce the price, and if you go to a health care organization that they haven't bartered with, you are going to pay more for your health care.

Health care insurance companies are not producing lists of what organizations they work with or prices for various medical procedures and sharing them openly. If you call them, they will usually tell you if your doctor is in network or out of network, meaning they will reimburse the out of network doctor/procedure less, leaving you to pay the larger difference out of pocket. If you change jobs, you could have a new health care insurance company and you won't know what you're going to pay. What other major purchases do we make in which we don't know the total cost involved? Yet this has been how health care insurance companies have been allowed to operate for many years.

The Politics of Price Transparency

As of January 2021, hospital systems are required to list the cost of procedures on their website. They will be required to do this in two ways or face a stiff daily fine if they do not cooperate.

1. As a comprehensive machine-readable file with all items and services.
2. In a display of shoppable services in a consumer-friendly format.

The Centers for Medicare and Medicaid Services (CMS) reports on their website: "hospitals' standard charges, including the rates they negotiate with insurance companies and the discounted price a hospital is willing to accept directly from a patient if paid in cash, must be publicly available, free of charge, and presented in a consumer-friendly display." [23] "Consumer-friendly" is the key undefined term here. Hospital systems have been fighting this change because that means they have to sift through information that Blue Cross,

United Healthcare, and the other various insurance agencies will cover for a procedure, creating a nightmare. How that information will be presented to the health care consumer in a consumer-friendly format remains to be seen.

There are two sides to the price transparency issue. The insurers and the hospitals proclaim price transparency will increase costs for your procedures. They argue that once this information becomes public, hospitals offering the same procedures/services at a lower price will raise their rates and health care will cost the consumer more.

This argument doesn't hold any merit, as both hospitals and insurance companies tend to make more money when charging higher prices. [24] The hospital systems have even sued CMS over the price transparency issue. The skeptics say the people will not take the time to use price transparency information and compare costs between various hospitals.

The other side believes that price transparency will drive down costs. It will aid in creating reference price models for employers and insurers. That way employers or insurers will know how much they must pay for a procedure. This incentivizes the consumer to shop, as they are responsible for any additional costs beyond that reference price. This occurred when Safeway used reference pricing for their employees, resulting in a 27 percent savings for lab tests and a 13 percent saving for imaging services.

The only way that price transparency in health care will work is if people are willing to pay attention. With the implementation of Obamacare, many people across America chose high deductible insurance plans as insurance prices skyrocketed. People who have a high deductible insurance plan are incentivized to shop for health care. That doesn't mean that the rest of us shouldn't be doing the same. For example, California adopted a reference pricing model for state employees. This resulted in a 14 percent increase in using lower priced health care facilities and a 21 percent decrease in costs. To single out one case that shows why this is true, consider a knee surgery. If you have total knee surgery at an outpatient clinic you will likely pay less than if you had it done as an inpatient in a hospital.

Another point that will drive this home is that Medicare rates can be as much as 60 percent below negotiated rates. We learned earlier in the book that Medicare covers 80 percent of total costs. This is important because if health care organizations are negotiating with Medicare, even with the 20 percent you personally pay, if you are private pay or your gap insurance has to cover, there is still a 40 percent margin that can be negotiated. Insurance companies and hospitals prefer that we as consumers not shop for our health care. The insurance companies and hospitals get paid on overall costs, which allows them to gain more profit at higher costs. [25]

A good example of using price transparency to decrease costs is total knee surgery. If you are an individual who elected to go with a high deductible health care plan due to rising insurance costs, it is beneficial for you to shop for your total knee surgery costs. Now that total knee surgeries can be done in Ambulatory Surgical Centers (ASC), you will likely pay less and possibly have a better quality outcome having your surgery at an ASC as opposed to a hospital. Plus, being an individual with a high deductible plan, you should be more incentivized to shop for your health care.

By not publishing the health care costs for medical procedures and various other costs, insurance companies and hospitals alike can have total control over what you pay. This can create a surprise when you get your hospital bill. Again, remember that you should look at every item on that bill to see if that's actually something you were given or a procedure performed. Not having to be accountable to anybody about what it will cost for you to have a procedure is the insurance company and hospital's preferred methodology.

This methodology also allows them to be in control of the data.

So, when an entrepreneur wants to study the cost for various procedures, they have to get it from the insurance companies, which is a very difficult task. Therefore, there isn't a lot of work going on to create greater efficiencies and driving down costs because there isn't easy access to the data. This is a recurring theme in health care. Not sharing the data means those who control it have less disruption to their current business model.

Some practical ways to search for the costs associated with a procedure/surgery is to start with the hospital or ASC that your surgeon is affiliated with. In my case, I did a web search, and my local hospital listed the prices at the very bottom of their web page, which was hard to find. Not surprising, as they really don't want me to access that information, but there is a section called pricing. Once I clicked on that section, there is a listing of pricing. The hospital makes this very difficult to find on their website, but once I found it I was asked questions about my insurance information to produce an estimate. Since I am insured by my employer, they were unable to provide me an estimate for total knee surgery. So I looked on their standard pricing sheet and the information I found there was in small print and arranged by procedure codes. This was not laid out in a consumer-friendly way, and it literally looked like this small example but went on forever.

[{"Procedure": "2500000015", "Code Type": "EAP", "Code": "", "Rev Code": "0250 - PHARMACY-GENERAL", "Procedure Description": "Hc Echo Contrast Agent", "Min /Max": "MIN", " Inpatient Gross Charge ": " 160.45 ", " Inpatient Negotiated Charge ": " 71.88 ", " Outpatient Gross Charge ": " 160.45 ", " Outpatient Negotiated Charge ": " 52.37 ", "TabName": "Hosp Deindentifed Payor MinMax"},{"Procedure": "2500000055", "Code Type": "EAP", "Code": "", "Rev Code": "0250 - PHARMACY-GENERAL", "Procedure Description": "Hc Sealant Evarrest Evt5044", "Min /Max": "MAX", " Inpatient Gross Charge ": " 3,310.15 ", "

Inpatient Negotiated Charge ": " 3,310.15 ", " Outpatient Gross Charge ": " 3,310.15 ", " Outpatient Negotiated Charge ": " 3,310.15 ", "TabName": "Hosp Deindentifed Payor MinMax"},{"Procedure": "2500000127", "Code Type": "EAP", "Code": "", "Rev Code": "0250 - PHARMACY-GENERAL", "Procedure Description": "Hc Anasept Antimicrobial Spray", "Min /Max": "MAX", " Inpatient Gross Charge ": " 42.00 ", " Inpatient Negotiated Charge ": " 42.05 ", " Outpatient Gross Charge ": " 42.05 ", " Outpatient Negotiated Charge ": " 42.05 ", "TabName": "Hosp Deindentifed Payor MinMax"},{"Procedure": "2500349041", "Code Type": "EAP", "Code": "CPT J3490", "Rev Code": "0250 - PHARMACY-GENERAL", "Procedure Description": "HC NM TAGAMET VIAL", "Min /Max": "MAX", " Inpatient Gross Charge ": " 14.00 ", " Inpatient Negotiated Charge ": " 13.50 ", " Outpatient Gross Charge ": " 13.50 ", " Outpatient Negotiated Charge ": " 13.50 ", "TabName": "Hosp Deindentifed Payor MinMax"},{"Procedure": "2550957700", "Code Type": "EAP", "Code": "CPT A9577", "Rev Code": "0272 - MEDICAL/SURGICAL SU

You can see that it would take a medical professional to figure this noise out. While there is no standard website for this information at the federal or state level, running a quick search at your local hospital and looking for pricing information is where I would suggest you start. If your search turns up a mess like my example, a simple call to the billing department of the hospital should bring clarity to the costs involved with the surgery or procedure. Also as previously mentioned, the Healthcare Blue Book can give you an idea of what a procedure/surgery should cost in your area. https://www.healthcare-bluebook.com/ui/consumerfront

This is why you have to be involved in your health care from every aspect. From price transparency to working as a collaborative member with your clinical team your involvement is key. Only through your involvement will you be able to drive down costs and create better health care outcomes. Now that the data is out to the general public, this is going to become a very big issue, and many entrepreneurs are going to offer forth solutions to assist you in driving down the health care costs and increasing your quality health care outcomes. I would strongly suggest you pay attention to this as it will evolve over the next few years now that the data is becoming available.

NURSING KNOWLEDGE

Be involved in your care. If you don't understand something keep asking questions until you do. Proactively do your research on costs of prescriptions, insurance, procedures and surgeries. An informed patient is safer patient with a healthier bottom line.

Part 3
A
Better
Healthcare
System

CHAPTER 9

Telehealth

The introduction of technology in the health care arena for the most part has the potential to assist you and your health care team to keep you healthy and at home. Hospitals will be facing drastic changes over the next decade as we move to a value-based care model. Health care costs decrease when a patient can be taken care of at home. Plus, patients with low-level issues have better health care outcomes at home, as the hospital environment can be stressful and unfamiliar. There is a movement called the hospital at home in which the hospital can make any room in your house into a hospital room. It is cost effective and patients are having better outcomes, so this is the wave of the future. To be taken care of at home, technology plays a huge role in getting information to your health care team. But with the use of technology comes some risks that you should be aware of. In part three we are going to explore telehealth, remote patient monitoring, the use of technology, your health care, genetic data, and the important movement toward value-based health care.

Telehealth is defined as the use of electronic information and telecommunication technologies to deliver care when you and the clinical staff are not in the same place at the same time. Through the use of platforms such as Facebook Messenger, Zoom, and Skype you can be seen by your clinical team. This wasn't always the case, but the COVID-19 crisis taught us the use of this technology was essential to decrease the risks of catching the virus. [26] But telehealth was not always this easy to use. Before the pandemic, the use of telehealth was extremely regulated. If you wanted to see a doctor in another state, that doctor had to have licensing privileges in the state in which you lived. Many states decided to reimburse telehealth, but it wasn't reimbursed in every state.

It took a pandemic and the federal government to step in and deregulate telehealth to make it more accessible to the general public. New York State was one of the first epicenters of COVID-19, due to the burden of care the clinicians experienced, telehealth was expanded to allow physicians from other states to care for non-COVID patients using telehealth. This prompted the government to ease its restrictions on telehealth and provide additional reimbursement for telehealth visits. [27]

By now 49 states (excluding Florida) have waivers, and the easing of the restrictions at the federal level looks like they may become permanent, although no legislation has yet been introduced. While most of the state waivers are set to expire in 2021 or when the state is past the current crisis, we're hoping in the medical community that these waivers become permanent, thus allowing us to care for more people more efficiently. [28]

In rural areas especially, access to health care can be limited. Telehealth is more efficient in caring for this patient population by avoiding lengthy drives to see their medical provider. The use of telehealth means the hospital or doctor's office staff doesn't have to clean the room between patients, which gives the medical team more time to see more patients. Using telehealth, the nurse and the physician can both be working from home and avoid their commute to the office. Plus, what we found in the middle of a pandemic is this is the safest way to provide care for non-emergency patients or a patient who does not need to be seen in the emergency department, such as someone suffering from a stroke or a heart attack. A stroke or a heart attack are serious medical conditions that can be lethal if not treated as emergencies.

To give you an idea of telehealth's skyrocketing growth, the

Veterans Administration (VA) went from 40,000 monthly mental telehealth visits to over 900,000 monthly visits during the pandemic. That is a 95 percent increase. Mental health visits can range from depression to personality disorders. The Department of Veterans Affairs Secretary Robert Wilkie stated that he felt productivity, patient satisfaction, and employee satisfaction went up. He also said on the medical front and particularly behavioral health, this is the future of health care.

NURSING KNOWLEDGE

Telehealth really took off in the mental or behavioral health arena. This is because there is really no hands on assessment being done. It's virtually counseling and medication management. It will become the wave of the future for caring for this type of patient population.

Telehealth also allowed the VA to expand its footprint in rural areas. The VA is also looking to expand its telehealth offerings by partnering with Walmart to implement telehealth facilities in their stores. Truly, telehealth and the COVID-19 pandemic have altered how care will be delivered in the future. [29]

During the COVID-19 pandemic, my wife had to use telehealth services for two doctor's appointments. She is the opposite of a techie, but on her own, she set up Zoom with the guidance of the clinical staff at her doctor's office and was able to log on and participate in her visits virtually. The process to get set up for telehealth on devices such as tablets or phones is very streamlined and not time consuming.

Telehealth Considerations

What must we consider as we look to expand telehealth, especially in rural areas? Some people don't have broadband access and may not be able to use the services quite as effectively as someone who lives in an urban setting. For this reason, the government allowed telehealth services to be delivered using just voice as opposed to voice and video. While that addresses the technology issue, there are other considerations such as people not having devices such as cell phones, computers, or tablets to use telehealth. Socioeconomic circumstances must be considered and some of that work has already begun.

When Congress passed the Coronavirus Aid, Relief, and Economic Security (CARES) Act in March 2020, it included $200 million in funding to the Federal Communications Commission (FCC) for a COVID-19 telehealth program that is assisting eligible health care providers to pay for telehealth services, as well as the devices they need to provide connected care. Using this money, the University of Pittsburgh Medical Center Children's Hospital was able to provide, without cost, the family of an infant organ transplant recipient a tablet complete with follow up instructions and cellular services, a microphone, and a camera.

To meet rural health care needs, in October 2020 FCC Chairman Ajit Pai announced the introduction of a $20 billion rural digital opportunity fund to aid in getting high quality broadband in up to six million locations in rural America. He added that for the first time in 22 years the FCC has increased the budget for a rural health care program that enables broadband connectivity to hospitals across the country. This is just the beginning of addressing the socioeconomic issues in providing access to health care to those in rural areas. [27]

Telehealth Benefits

While we have seen some changes to telehealth, such as increased usage of telehealth and increased funding for telehealth brought on by the COVID-19 pandemic, we have yet to see a national strategy in place. A doctor is a doctor, after all, and it doesn't matter if I see one in New York or North Carolina. Although there are some differences in how medications can be prescribed, the standards of care do not change from state to state.

Telehealth will aid in better health care access, as going to the doctor's office often means taking a half or full day off from work while you wait in an office with other sick people for your turn to see the doctor. I don't know about you, but I never liked going to the doctor's office. With telehealth, appointments are on time for the most part and do not eat up a large portion of your day. Combined with mail-order pharmacies, this will be the most efficient and safest way for you to receive care.

Another factor to consider is seeing a doctor is usually less costly than going to an urgent care facility to address your medical needs. [27] In my case I relocated from Greensboro, NC, to a town just outside of Charlotte. I haven't changed doctors because my physician and I, who is located in Greensboro, have a good working relationship and partner on my care. His office recently implemented telehealth and I recently used the telehealth platform for my annual wellness visits. It saves me the one hour and thirty-minute drive to see my doctor.

Remote Patient Monitoring

The day is coming when doctors will not be paid according to the number of patients they see but instead will be reimbursed for the quality of their work. In the industry, we call this value-based care. In other words, the doctor will collect their reimbursement for keeping you out of the hospital. That's quite a shift to how we are currently giving care. Greater amounts of care will be given in the home, a shift we're already beginning to see. Why not? Wouldn't you rather be in your home when you're sick? I know I would. Remote patient monitoring and telehealth will be very important components for caring for patients outside of the hospital. The future is going to look very different than it does right now.

Take the example of congestive heart failure patients (CHF). These patients have many signs and symptoms that manifest themselves. As their CHF worsens, the patient will begin to gain weight, have fluid or edema to their lower legs, have increased shortness of breath. As a result, they don't walk as many monitored steps. Currently, once these symptoms become acute, the patient shows up in the emergency department or the physician's office, depending on the severity. This taxes the healthcare system, as it's a very costly way to treat these patients.

The signs and symptoms could have been proactively managed at home through telehealth to avoid the patient needing to go to the doctor's office or the emergency department. Monitoring tools such as wireless blood pressure cuffs, pulse oximeters, wearables such as Fitbit's or Apple watches, and wireless scales are being used to monitor this patient population before they experience a crisis. The information from these tools is fed up in the cloud via the internet or using cellular technology, where it is then monitored by nurse navigators. When the nurse sees that the patient isn't walking as many steps, or their oxygen levels appear to be going down, or they notice a five-pound weight gain over the past week, they can intervene earlier.

This vital clinical information allowing the clinical staff to intervene can prevent a full-blown congestive heart failure (CHF) event.

Notifying the patient can be done in a variety of ways such as texting, telephone calls, or email from the nurse navigator. The patient's medication may also be adjusted. This is one of the ways in which value-based care works. Also, insurance companies welcome this proactive clinical approach as a way to drive down costs.

There is an increasing emphasis on keeping the patients healthy as opposed to hospital care or treating episodes of illness. With revenue from health care expected to reach $3.5 trillion in 2022, a telehealth strategy is a must for any organization. Chronic disease management such as CHF, diabetes, hypertension, etc., consumes about 85 percent of all health care dollars. A full-blown congestive heart failure (CHF) crisis, for which a patient is admitted to the hospital, is much more costly than monitoring their CHF symptoms using technology and intervening early. [30]

Plus, it leads to better health care for the patient. Who wants to go to the hospital when they can proactively manage their chronic disease from the comfort of their own home? In the past, people were much more hesitant to use remote monitoring and telehealth, but the COVID-19 pandemic changed that. In fact, 75 percent of patients with chronic diseases in the United States say that they would be willing to try remote monitoring devices if their physician recommended them. [31]

Placing Patients on a Spectrum

You should be aware of a term called population health. This is used to create registries or lists of patients who are managing a chronic disease. This aids the doctors in managing their patients. This technology can also list the patients that the nurse navigator needs to call, based on parameters such as increased blood sugar levels in patients with diabetes. The system sees that these patients need to rise to the top of the list, and the nurse knows they need to intervene on them first. These systems can also predict if you're at risk for an acute episode, which may land you in the hospital, by sorting through your data and assigning you a risk number. These population health registries monitor your present and past history. If you are a diabetic patient and your blood sugar is elevated five days out of seven each week, you will receive a higher risk score than a diabetic patient whose blood sugar remains within normal parameters every day. This alerts the health care team that you need to be closely monitored.

In one of the newer innovations, with your permission, a doctor can have you added to a consumer relationship management (CRM) software platform. This allows the health care team to communicate with you via text, email, or whatever your preferred communication type is. This allows them to push out reminders such as scheduling a colonoscopy, because we all remember to do that, right? It can remind you to get your flu shot or remind you of various health care appointments or your doctor's appointment the next day. This technology also makes you feel more connected to your health care team.

As baby boomers get older, technology will be the driving force that allows them to live longer more productive independent lives. The data shows that about 125,000 Americans die every year from not taking their medications. Just to put this in perspective that's about double the number of Americans who die from automobile accidents. For Americans over 65 years of age, 33 to 69 percent of hospital admissions are due to patients not taking their medications. 40 percent of nursing home admissions occur because Americans are unable to reliably self-medicate at home. With one in four people over 65 living alone, telehealth solutions could allow them to live independently longer. [32]

If a home health nurse visits a patient once a week and loads their medication-monitoring device with a week's worth of their medications, the system can notify the patient when to take their medication by several means. It could be an alarm, text message or if the device is interfaced into Google mini or Alexa, it could be delivered verbally. These systems are also capable of alerting the home health agency, a relative, or the doctor's office when the patient doesn't take their medications.

How does this affect you? If you have a chronic disease, your doctor may ask you to use a remote patient monitoring tool such as a glucometer, which is used to monitor blood sugar in diabetic patients. The information could be sent to the clinical team for their review, and they may make changes to your medications based on this information. As a nurse, I would strongly encourage you to manage any chronic disease using these tools. They will increase your quality of life and allow you to avoid nasty germy hospitals and doctor's offices. It should decrease the amount of time you spend going to doctor's appointments and should only cost you minutes a day of your time.

NURSING KNOWLEDGE

If you have a good internet system at home do not be afraid to use technology to monitor your health care. Using technology will allow you to be cared for and monitored at home instead of in an unfamiliar environment such as a hospital.

Caring for patients in their homes is the future of health care. It's reported that home health care will grow five percent from 2014 to 2024. 1.26 million individuals worked in home health care in 2014, and that number is expected to rise to 2.02 million in 2024. Being cared for at home is a less costly model that is here to stay. [33]

Taking care of patients in their homes, of course, is not a new concept. It started in the 1990's, but due to issues with reimbursement from Medicare and insurance companies, it didn't catch on. It took a pandemic and the federal government to waive requirements for how hospitals get paid for care in the home. This care is called "hospital at home."

I'll bet most of you didn't know this was an option, but many hospitals are beginning to adopt this model. It makes sense for hospitals because it can prevent overcrowding during peak flu seasons or a pandemic. Patients have better outcomes, they fall less in their home environment and they can eat whatever they want. Many times, when someone is admitted to a hospital, their mobility decreases as there is really nowhere to go. Being cared for at home, they can go outside, take a walk and sleep in their own bed without the sounds of alarms going off.

For the payors, the care the patient receives costs between 29-38 percent less without any difference in survival or hospital readmissions. Since the payors are laser-focused on reducing the spending for health care, they are awaiting the government to waive the requirements for where a patient receives care. I predict that in the future hospitals will consist only of emergency departments, intensive care units (ICUs), step down beds which is where a patient is cared for before they become a low acuity (less sick) patient, and home care. [34]

You may be thinking, "Will I get the same level of care in my home that I would get in the hospital?" To answer that we have to explore a few variables. First of all, you should never opt for home care if there isn't someone who can assist in your care. Next, these companies or even healthcare systems that offer hospital at home services can turn any room in the house into a hospital room, complete with oxygen tanks, medical supplies, and almost anything else you may need. For example, one system used a watch-like device to monitor COVID-19 patients. When a patient's oxygen levels dropped and their blood pressure spiked, the nurse navigator called the patient and told them to go to the emergency department. After a week's stay at the hospital, the patient was discharged and sent home. [35]

They can also bring x-ray machines into your house, have nurses visit you, and do daily rounds using internet technology. Daily rounds are where your doctor and health care team goes over your vital signs and labs and discusses your care plan with you virtually. This is the perfect marriage of technology and clinical care in which patients can derive the benefit of staying at home while their chronic care is being managed or they are recovering from an illness. Many of these programs are linked to a 24/7 monitoring system to monitor your vital signs and other pertinent health care data in real-time. Plus, you have a button you can press at any time for emergency help. [34]

In another push, software is changing the ordering of the equipment you may need, transportation, and even meal ordering. Although this is a new technology many electronic medical record vendors are turning to companies who perform these services to streamline the amount of interaction needed with medical equipment suppliers, transportation companies such as Lyft and Uber, and providers of proper nutrition.

One startup company, Xealth, has partnered with the two largest electronic medical record companies in the world to provide these services. The company also professes to allow tracking of the services being provided so the health care organization can understand how many blood pressure cuffs they prescribed or how many Lyft/Uber rides were provided to patients last month. This technology is relatively new, but in the world of being cared for at home it will become an invaluable tool. [36]

The use of technology in health care is game changing. This will allow more people to be cared for and monitored at home. Like anything in health care, the use of technology is slowly evolving after being regulated for so long by the federal and state governments. COVID-19 changed the landscape of how technology is used in health care for the better. In fact, it is probably the only silver lining of the pandemic. Not every doctor embraces the use of technology, and older doctors may be more hesitant. Younger doctors, though not as experienced, embrace technology much more readily. These are factors you will want to consider as you chose a doctor. Being a part of your health care team, you will want to ask the doctor if your care can be provided in the home environment.

NURSING KNOWLEDGE

You are in control of your health care. Your health care team should work hand in hand with you to manage your health care. Now that you are educated on the technology options available to you, don't be afraid to suggest them to your health care team.

CHAPTER 10

Technology

Beyond telehealth, medical technology has been expanding for over a decade to automate health care. We are presently in the phase of standardized evidence based medicine. Medical professionals have done the research and understand how to achieve the same outcome for many conditions. If you went for a knee replacement, for instance, your doctor would have a standardized order set for a knee replacement which would cover 80 percent of what you needed for the hospitalization. He would then adjust the additional 20 percent for you as an individual having the surgery. Your nurse would also be working off from protocols they would use to provide your nursing care. An example is getting you up to walk as soon as possible because if you lie in the bed after surgery, you are at risk for developing pneumonia and/or blood clots due to inactivity and the anesthesia you received during your surgery.

It's important to note that from start to finish, it takes on average 17 years to move something like a best practice such as increased mobility in the example above into an evidence based model. The reason for this is medical studies need to be done to provide evidence that getting you up and moving after surgery decreases the likelihood that you will develop a blood clot or pneumonia and that can take a very long time. This is why Amazon, Google, and Microsoft are jumping into health care. It is a three trillion dollar industry and Amazon, Google and Microsoft are the data masters. They want in because there is a lot of money to be made in health care. With the introduction of these major players, the data will move much faster than it has in the past. Of course, the healthcare system is putting in place safeguards to protect your data, such as stripping it of personal information before giving it to researchers.

To assist in this development, we are moving into a model of using artificial intelligence (AI) and machine learning in your care. Artificial intelligence mimics human behavior to fulfill a task. A good example of that is I wear a tracking device that counts my steps. Via AI my steps go right into my health care account, which incentivizes me because I can reduce my insurance premium for every 5,000 steps I walk. If I wasn't using AI I would have to manually enter my steps every day to reduce my insurance premium.

Machine learning (ML) uses AI data to run algorithms to predict outcomes. A good example is the rapid response team model we talked about earlier in the book. Using ML your data in an electronic medical record (EMR) is constantly being analyzed to proactively look for deterioration in your medical picture such as sepsis. Once parameters are identified that are abnormal such as a high heart rate, elevated temperature, and low blood pressure which are signs of sepsis ML can quickly suggest to the nurse or the doctor how you should be treated. This is an important breakthrough as this gives the newer clinician who may not be as seasoned as the 20 year veteran a tool to quickly intervene in the patient's care. The more data run through machine learning the more accurate the algorithms become. Don't worry, nothing will ever replace the clinical staff, as someone has to personally supervise your care, but with automation, we can make your care streamlined and safer. [37]

The COVID-19 crisis has provided several good examples of machine learning and AI. In the early weeks, it was difficult to conduct testing as test supplies were in demand. Amazon's Web Services (AWS), their cloud computing division, partnered with UC San Diego Health to set up a machine learning algorithm through which patients' chest x-rays could be read to see if they had COVID-19.

They studied x-rays from patients in China and the U.S. and then, using the algorithm, they developed heat maps which aided in looking for the probability of pneumonia. They implemented this in ten days, and within the next week, they had read close to 20,000 images.

In one case, a chest x-ray was performed on a patient who came to the emergency department with diarrhea and a fever. The x-ray was fine, but when it was put through this algorithm, it came back as COVID-19 positive. They tested the patient and indeed he was positive for COVID-19. This is just one of many innovations going on in health care to assist the clinical staff in producing safer care. [38]

In another attempt to detect the COVID-19 virus, there is ongoing research into the use of wearables. This kind of out-of-the-box thinking is necessary as there have been huge testing shortages during the pandemic. There have been multiple attempts by experts to detect COVID-19 from various devices. One company created a patch that will measure body temperature. Yet it was found that body temperature alone is not enough to diagnose COVID-19, as half of the people who had the virus did not present with an increase in their temperature. Research is being conducted on a patch that could detect your heart rate, and that looks promising because research shows that a high heart rate, while you are sitting or lying down, increased amounts of sleeping, and decreased physical activity, are indicators for the flu, which are also symptoms of COVID-19. A biomedical engineering company created a patch that checks for temperature, heart rate, body motion, and chest movement. That's because many COVID-19 patients had coughing rates averaging 100 coughs an hour.

Although there is promise in the use of technology to alert the medical community to the possibility of the flu or COVID-19, a doctor still needs to diagnose it. Although we centered on COVID-19, as technology rushed in to aid the clinical staff during a worldwide pandemic, technology is also used in other areas in health care. If you are in the hospital, hooked up to a monitor, chances are your heart rate, blood pressure and respiratory rate are being written right into your patient record through an interface or bridge between the electronic medical record (EMR) and the monitor system. The nurse simply has to verify your vital signs before it becomes a part of your medical record.

NURSING KNOWLEDGE

Technology is an important aspect of your care but will never replace your doctor or nurse who are highly trained to manage your care. Health care is a team sport and you are part of that team.

Electronic Medical Records

Electronic medical records, or EMR's as they are known in the industry, have automated how patient data is collected and shared with your health care team. This is important because when documentation and health care data were on paper, it was very hard to study the data. Medicine is ever evolving, changing as new information is received. This drives better care as we learn more and more about how to treat specific diseases such as diabetes, pneumonia, and congestive heart failure.

The first step was removing the pen from the doctor's hand. I cannot tell you how many times a doctor's order was transcribed incorrectly because of their terrible handwriting. I can recall when a doctor with lousy handwriting scribbled some orders that were extremely difficult to read. Couple that with the fact that this doctor was not the most pleasant individual on the planet and calling him to clarify his orders usually meant he was going to yell at you. So I decided to take care of my other patients and call him later. As it turned out, I forgot and the order was for an intravenous (IV) antibiotic, which meant the patient's care was delayed by 24 hours when the doctor realized the medication hadn't been given.

Through the use of EMR's when a doctor places an order it is legible and goes to the correct individual caring for the patient. If it's for an X-ray the order is routed to radiology and the nurse who is caring for the patient. The use of EMR's removed the potential for human error as previously the orders went to a unit clerk who entered them into whatever system was being used and then notified the nurse who had to review the orders. The orders now went directly to the caregiver or department. If that were the case I would not have missed that IV antibiotic and the patient would have gone home sooner.

While the change from paper to electronic medical records (EMRs) was disruptive, it was needed, as data in paper charts were difficult to extract. For example, before EMR's, if I wanted historic data on you from a previous admission I would have to request an old chart from the medical records department and wait until that information was delivered. Then I would have to spend time reviewing the chart to gather the information I needed. Through the use of EMR's, I can now trend your data such as blood sugar measurements in diabetic patients. I may see that your blood sugar increases on Monday morning readings and ask you what changes you make in your diet Sunday nights. This would be very hard to accomplish if your data were in a paper record. Using data to study trends in health care is essential to producing better treatments and understanding underlying factors about how diseases progress.

With the implementation of electronic medical records (EMRs), a burden is placed on the care team in documenting your care. That's because most doctors and nurses would rather care for patients than enter data. But digitizing the patient care record was essential to quickly get to the data and use it to drive your care. In the future, you may sit down with your doctor at your next appointment, and they may mention they have a recorder set up to record the conversation. The recorder captures key bits of information, such as your reason for seeing the doctor. It then populates the doctor's note with that information so they can review it and sign off on it. This saves the doctor time, but also they aren't dependent on having to remember everything you said. Without digitizing the patient care record breakthroughs such as the example above wouldn't be possible.

This phase of health care is in its infancy but has the potential to reduce caregiver burnout. That occurs when your caregivers, which could be your physician, nurse, or even a relative caring for you, are overloaded with work and/or other responsibilities. Work life invades home life and the clinician can't keep up. Maybe they are missing their children's ball games or dance recitals due to work. Research shows that 80% of doctors surveyed believe this technology could reduce caregiver burnout. [39]

In another example, an electronic medical device now connects to intravenous (IV) pumps, which are used to deliver IV medications through your veins. The doctor writes the order in the EMR, and all the nurse has to do is scan your wristband, scan the pump and verify the order on the pump. The nurse then starts your medication. In the old days, the nurse would read the order and have to enter it into the pump to start your medication. The nurse had to transcribe the order to the IV pump correctly to avoid a medication error. I know from working at the bedside that I wasn't always my sharpest the 11th hour into a 12 hour shift. This type of technology helps medical staff to give safe, efficient care by reducing the steps in the process.

Before the use of technology, your care depended on how much knowledge your health care team possessed and their skill set. There is so much new knowledge coming out in health care that it's impossible to keep up with all of it. Through the use of technology, we can equip the new graduate nurse or the new intern with the seasoned knowledge base of a 20 year veteran. When you are admitted to the hospital, technology can alert your nurse that you are deteriorating by looking at your labs, taking into consideration your vital signs, etc. It may alert your nurse in the EMR or on a smaller device such as a cellular phone to consider, for example, sepsis and call your doctor.

There are many tools used to predict the severity of illness in health care. One such tool is called Modified Early Warning System (MEWS). This system provides the nurse a risk score, and generally, if the patient's risk score is higher, there is a greater chance that the patient will end up in the Intensive Care Unit (ICU) or die. This assists the nurse and provides an evidence based tool that lets the nurse know they need to closely monitor the patient.

Timely Intervention

In health care, the faster we can get the data, the faster we can intervene, thus providing better patient outcomes. Some hospital systems give nurses and doctors cell phones to aid in better care. If you see a nurse in a hospital texting on a cell phone, they may be giving the doctor information about your condition. These same phones push out notifications of critical lab values at the time they hit the electronic medical record (EMR). In the past I might be caring for patients and log on to the EMR several hours after the lab results came in, losing that precious time in which the team could have intervened quickly.

It also makes the staff more efficient. In the past, if I wanted to report a finding to your doctor, I would have to walk down to the whiteboard with the doctor's information, located at the nursing station, which might be quite a distance from where I was taking care of a patient. I would look at which doctor was on call and page the doctor. If the doctor didn't call back right away because they were busy, such as during a procedure, I would return to patient care. Often the doctor would call back while I was doing a sterile dressing change and was unable to take the call.

With this new technology, I can simply look the doctor up in the directory and securely text him the information. I can see when the doctor reads the text and hopefully the doctor responds. The Joint Commission (TJC), a regulatory body many hospitals are affiliated with, does not allow the doctor to order anything via text at this point in time, so if the doctor is giving the nurse an order, they can enter it in the EMR or call the nurse with it if the doctor isn't near a computer. As we have discussed previously the faster the information gets to your doctor or nurse the quicker they can intervene.

I remember talking with a Chief Nursing Officer (CNO) who told me that the alerts in her EMR for a life threatening condition called sepsis weren't working correctly. They were firing to the nurses and doctors hours later, thus leaving the team less time to intervene. When I traced the problem in the EMR, it turned out that the nursing staff was taking the patient's vital signs but not entering them into the EMR until up to four hours later. They weren't being neglectful. Rather, they were busy with other patients and couldn't get to a computer in a timely fashion. Once we realized that was the problem, we explored the use of technology and the nursing staff's workflow (how the work gets done) to feed the vital signs directly into the EMR when they were taken. This is a much more efficient method and helped to decrease their sepsis rates.

The faster information is exchanged, the better the patient outcomes are. While the automation of healthcare systems was needed, it was disruptive. That gave the healthcare system the foundation through the use of the EMR and automated ordering to implement technology that delivers information faster and more efficiently. Getting the right information to the right health care team member in the most efficient manner will produce better patient outcomes.

NURSING KNOWLEDGE

When choosing a hospital an important question to ask is how they are using technology to drive down mortality (death) rates and find patients who are deteriorating (getting sicker). Now that you have been educated on this topic you can make an informed decision.

CHAPTER 11

Who Owns Your Healthcare Data?

In the old days, patients were discouraged from reading their charts unless a clinician was sitting next to them. We did this because medicine has its own language. Based in Latin, many of the terms would confuse a patient, not to mention various degrees of lousy handwritten doctor's notes. We were the keepers of your health care data. That's changing, and it should change as you should have more control of your data.

Although electronic medical records (EMRs) free up your data, it also opens the possibility of more risk. [40] Just as sharing private information with Instagram or Facebook brings risks, you don't want your health care data to fall into the hands of the wrong entities. You have to be diligent and protect your data. There are laws in place to assist with this, but the process is tricky. Remember my emergency department visit earlier in the book? When I called the hospital and requested they transfer my records to my doctor's office, they informed me that the doctor, not the patient, had to request the record be transferred. I found that to be a little archaic. After all, it's my data, right? Maybe and maybe not. Let's explore the complexities of how your data is accessed by you and others.

Data Protection

The Health Insurance Portability and Accountability Act (HIPAA) was passed in 1996 to protect patients' health care data. HIPAA was created to modernize the flow of health care information, set parameters around your personal health care information (PHI) and how it is used by health care entities and most importantly health care insurers. It put into place safeguards to protect your PHI from fraud, theft and addressed limitations on health care insurance coverage. Basically, it combats waste and abuse in health insurance and health care delivery. [41]

That act was passed more than two decades ago, and many in health care believe it needs a serious overhaul to address the rise in digitalization that has occurred since then, as the sharing of information has proven to be so beneficial to improved patient outcomes. When the bill was first passed, I was in the early stage of my nursing career. The frontline staff was educated to be very careful where we discussed patient information—i.e., elevators or hallways where other patients or their family members could overhear the conversation. We were told if we violated this in any way, we could be heavily fined and possibly terminated.

Everyone was so paranoid that often when family members called to check on their loved ones, they would be told the clinician could not give out information over the phone. To alleviate the frustration, codes that could be words or numbers were developed for the release of information. You would set these up with the patient and their family in advance. This ensured that the person on the other end of the line was indeed who they said they were and was entitled to receive the patient's information.

I will pick up my request to have my information shared with my doctor's office. If I had gone to the hospital, they would have released my record to me if I signed their hospital-generated release form. According to HIPAA, they had up to 30 days to release my information. Yet that meant going to the hospital in the middle of a pandemic. Once I asked my doctor's office to request my data, they sent me a form via my patient portal, which is a secure platform to get my test results, send my doctor an email, or request prescription refills. I had to print the form, sign it, and send it back to them via snail mail. I asked if I could scan it and send it back via the portal and never received a response. The process of the hospital and my doctor's office were cumbersome and somewhat archaic.

I am hardly alone in my exasperation. At my present company, the previous Chief Executive Officer's (CEO) wife had cancer. Although we were on the front lines of automating health care, he literally had to drag shopping bags of her records to each specialist's appointments. That's because even with the automation of health care records, it was very difficult to share the electronic medical records between the various systems. If the CEO of one of the largest EMR companies in the world had to drag his wife's medical records around the country, think about what it must be like for someone without his knowledge.

NURSING KNOWLEDGE

Most EMR's do not communicate well with each other. If your doctor's office uses one EMR and the hospital uses a different EMR chances of seamlessly exchanging information between the two systems will prove to be difficult.

Healthcare and Big Data Companies

Enter big tech companies like Apple to the rescue. In terms of the big data gurus, most patients and health care professionals find Apple has more integrity in terms of privacy than their competitors. Google and Facebook use your online presence to drive you to the merchandise they think you will buy, and both organizations have had their fair share of data integrity issues. [42] Since their health records application was introduced in March 2018, Apple has worked with 200 healthcare organizations, such as UC San Diego Health and the Veterans Administration. [43] Apple's CEO Tim Cook has stated that Apple has avoided acquiring user data to sell ads. [42]

The Apple app allows doctors and nurses to view patient's data and treat them more holistically. It can interface with the patient's electronic medical record (EMR) and provide information such as how often the patient exercises as well as previous lab work and diagnoses. For the patient it keeps them informed and involved in their care. They can often communicate with their care team right from the app. This is a game changer for a patient admitted to the emergency department who is unresponsive. If the care team can access the app they will have the patient's previous medical information, which will aid them in treating the patient better, such as knowing what the patient is allergic to and any other previous medical history.

Apple is not without scrutiny, however. The *Wall Street Journal* reported that several top fitness apps available for the iPhone did send personal information, such as heart rate, to Facebook. [42] Apple argues that these are third party apps, meaning Apple did not develop them but allowed them to interface into the Apple platform. Apple's main point is even though they exist on the Apple platform, they do not connect to the Apple health record app, meaning there is no exchange of data. Apple goes on to say that you have to allow any app on their Apple health record your permission before they can access your data. Another point is that the data is not kept in the cloud, so it's not generally available for hackers to go after. Instead, the data is downloaded to your devices such as your phone or tablet. [42]

While it's pretty enticing to have all your health care information on your phone and available to your providers, especially if you have a complex health care situation, you must weigh the benefits against the risks. Some education is needed to make the user aware. They should do their research on any third party application before permitting them to access their health care data. Putting your personal health care information into any technology company's hands requires trust, so just make sure you understand fully how third parties integrate into the application and proceed with caution. [42]

However, it is promising that big names in health care such as Johns Hopkins, Cedars-Sinai, and the Veterans Administration are working with Apple. It's also comforting to know that a survey at UC San Diego Health revealed that 78 percent of the users of Apple health records were satisfied with the app. [43] The Department of Health and Human Services (HHS) recently released their Federal Health IT Strategic Plan for 2020-2025. In this plan, they are pushing to make your health care information accessible on your smartphone. The process that they will use is not clearly defined at this time, but it looks like this will eventually be the new normal. [44]

Data Sharing (Interoperability)

One of the largest electronic medical records (EMR) companies pushed back on recent legislation for sharing of your data between electronic medical records. This legislation was originally proposed in 2019, allowing you, the consumer, access to your electronic medical record data. The EMR company's major rival wanted to allow your information to be shared across electronic medical record systems. The CEO of Epic Systems drafted a letter for clients to be sent to the Department of Health and Human Services (HHS) saying that these changes would be burdensome to the industry. Yet some of the top healthcare systems running Epic did not sign the letter, and the HHS kept to their goal of making it easier to for the patient to access their own EMR data. [45]

COVID-19 changed how your data is shared. At the beginning of the pandemic, apps were offered to allow contact tracing or the ability to know if you were near an infected person and for how long, using your phone and Bluetooth technology. A participant downloaded an app on their Apple or Android device and opted in to allow the app to send and receive information. Virginia was the first state to offer such an app, and even though half a million people downloaded the app, that was less than 10 percent of their population. Low adoption of this technology produced low protection from infection.

It was recently announced that Apple and Android devices will now include this technology in their future operating systems. What this means is that these operating systems will push out a notification, asking you if you want to opt-in and gather your information if you decide to opt-in. The thought is more people will opt-in if they do not have to download and maintain an app. The underlying question is: should you opt-in?

Both platforms say they will not collect the identity or the location of the user, but the issue goes beyond that. [46] Sometimes technology can produce false positives or negatives, meaning the information may not always be accurate. So if the technology shows that you have been exposed to the virus, can you handle the uncertainty of receiving that information until you can get an actual medical diagnosis? For someone who thinks every little cold will end up being pneumonia, causing them to be put on a ventilator in the hospital, they may want to think twice about opting in. For someone who wants the information and will use it wisely to limit their exposure to older relatives until they can properly be tested, this might make sense.

It will be interesting to get the research on false positives/negatives from the first round of using this technology to better understand its accuracy. One reason this country has failed so miserably at controlling the pandemic was the lack of contact tracing. That being said, technology would be a wonderful way to track a virus if it works as designed.

Let's move beyond this specific example to further understand the complications of medical data. While you do own your health data, your doctor or hospital owns your medical record. That's where the medical record was created and is stored. Your health care provider is still the gatekeeper of your health care data, just in a different way. They can share your information with an insurance company for billing inquiries. They are also able to disclose your information to law enforcement or public health agencies.

Expanding access raises a host of concerns. For one, your employer may ask you to take a wellness exam, including blood work and vital signs. They can also administer a drug test and keep that information on file. Then think about companies who self-insure. They have even more of your personal health information. Employers aren't supposed to act on your wellness information, but they do have access to it. That has led to widespread problems. For instance, AOL Chief Executive Officer (CEO) Tim Armstrong in 2015 blamed benefit cuts on two employees with "distressed babies." Others in the company were able to connect the dots and figure out who these two mothers were. This led to employees confronting the two mothers as the reason their health care costs increased. One of the mothers publicly denounced Armstrong's inability to keep her baby's health care information confidential. If Armstrong had been a nurse practicing under HIPPA, he could have lost his job. Yet as a CEO he retained his position and felt no impact from his actions. [40]

Controlling Your Data

One of the things that you can do is ask your doctor for an accounting of disclosures. This is a list of times they shared your information with another person or organization. This will help you understand how your information is being used.

Also, if something is incorrect in your health care information, you have the right to ask your doctor to change it. Do this formally and in writing, keeping a dated copy for yourself. The doctor will have 60 to 90 days to make the change. If your doctor doesn't agree to make the change, they will have to, at a minimum, record the disagreement in your medical record.

If for some reason you feel your data was used improperly, you should file a complaint with your doctor or hospital, your insurance company, the Department of Health and Human Services, and/or your state's Attorney General's office. Usually, the privacy notice you receive when you agree to be treated by the doctor or the hospital will tell you how to file a complaint. [40]

Again, health care data is complicated. While you own it, the health care data can be used without your permission in certain cases. You should think seriously about sharing any health care data with free third party apps, as they will more than likely sell your data. There is no such thing as a free lunch. Never post health care data to a social media site, as that's fair game for anyone to access. I can't tell you how many times I see friends and family post up procedures they had done: scars, cuts and bruises, and various other cringe worthy health care information. Keep your health care data private and always check the privacy policies before you share your data electronically.

NURSING KNOWLEDGE

Keep your health care data private. Avoid publicly exposing your data on social media or any other medium. Research third party apps such as Fitbit who is now owned by Google to see how they are using your data. Being an informed consumer will aid you in closely guarding your health care data.

Data Breaches

You should also be aware of data breaches. These are happening more often than ever before. Sometimes it occurs at a hospital, where data hackers will get access to patient data. They then ask for a ransom to not publish the data, and the majority of the time the hospital pays it. Healthcare systems try to keep this quiet, as it shows their vulnerability. In 2016 a journalist contacted an orthopedic clinic in Georgia to notify them that a database of their patient records was online and available for sale. A hacker then contacted the clinic two days later and demanded a ransom to return the stolen database. Even after paying a ransom, there are no guarantees that the hacker did not sell the personal information, which includes sensitive health care data, names, and addresses as well as social security numbers. [47]

In one of the largest data breach cases, Premera Blue Cross, based in Washington state, had to pay the office of the Health and Human Services (HHS) Office for Civil Rights a whopping 6.85 million dollars for a data breach that affected 10.4 million people. The hackers used an email program to install malware that gave them access to Premera's information technology system (IT) for nine months. The protected health care information included patient's names, addresses, email addresses, social security numbers, bank account information as well as their health care information. Although there are regulated risk analyses that the company was supposed to perform, they didn't do the analysis, which left them vulnerable to an attack. [47] While this is an extreme use of your health care and personal data without your permission it does happen. Asking any health care entity that you may be dealing with for information on how they safeguard your data is something you should seriously consider.

Genetic Testing: The Pros and Cons

You may be saying to yourself: why are we covering genetic testing? I am never going to get genetically tested. Well, if you ever spit into a tube and sent a sample to ancestry.com, then you have been genetically tested. Over 19 million people as of the fall of 2019 sent their genetic information to companies like ancestry.com and 23andMe. These companies have safeguards in place, like storing your personal data away from your genetic information. But it is what happens after your data leaves these companies that you should be concerned about. They share or sell de-identified genetic information to researchers and drug companies. Once you have given them your genetic information, it is extremely hard to control.

Your genetic information is your biological footprint, your unique genetic code. The information is specific to you, the individual. It can tell you (and others) what illness you are at risk for. While there are many pros to learning about your genetic information, such as being relieved if a disease runs in your family and it turns out this disease is not in your genetic makeup. Plus, if something is found it can be dealt with proactively. The information can help you make informed decisions and maybe even reduce some unnecessary screenings. Some people use the information to decide if they want to have children.

Genetic testing can only provide a limited amount of information about an inherited condition. The test itself cannot determine if the person will become symptomatic. The test will only show you what could occur, not necessarily what will occur.

There are many cons to genetic testing, and if you are considering it I would recommend that you talk with a genetic counselor before the test. Some of the cons are people may feel anxious or depressed if they discover they are at high risk for developing a genetic disease. It can create tension in families as the genetic makeup of other family members can be similar which may reveal similar areas of risk for those family members. [48]

Genetic Discrimination

Genetic discrimination is defined as employment or insurance discrimination due to your genetic information. While there are laws in place to address these concerns there are some loopholes. The Genetic Information Nondiscrimination Act (GINA) passed in 2008 seeks to address these concerns. There are two parts to this act. One deals with insurance discrimination, and the second deals with employment discrimination for companies over 15 employees. [49]

The insurance discrimination deals with your health care insurer having access to this information but does not cover secondary insurance such as life insurance. This can carry a loophole as many health care insurers also have a division that sells life insurance. This could be problematic. If you are predisposed to a condition such as breast cancer, Huntington's disease, or any other genetic diseases or disorders and you apply for a life insurance policy and the insurance company has your genetic information. You could be denied the coverage or charged a higher rate for the coverage. [48]

To address the employment genetic discrimination let's imagine I am a small business owner of a construction firm with 13 employees and my firm is growing. I want to add another employee and I have interviewed two individuals. While in most states I cannot ask them about their current state of health, I can run an internet search on them to see what they are posting on social media and may even find access to their genetic code.

Let's imagine I do find their genetic code information, and one of my prospects has the increased potential to develop breast cancer while the other prospect's information looks good. Suppose I have a family and small children and I am concerned that if I hire this person and the insurance company has access to this information, my insurance rates may go up. I decide not to hire this prospect. That is totally legal, as I do not have over 15 employees, but it is also genetic discrimination. Your data is not like your credit card, which can be canceled at any time. Once your data is exposed, it is out there for good. [48]

Many people are downloading their private genetic information from sites like Ancestry.com and 23andMe into databases like GEDMatch, which allows the genetic information or DNA to be sifted and matched. [49] People use this information to find other relatives that may not have been tested in the same database, such as Ancestry.com. If you had a cousin who used 23andMe while you used Ancestry.com, you would never be matched because your genetic information would be in two different databases. Also, people are using databases like GEDMatch because Ancestry.com and 23andMe are not going to give you the contact information for your matches. [49]

One grisly example is how data was used to track down and convict the Golden State Killer. He was responsible for four murders and dozens of rapes in the San Francisco area back in the 1980's. Investigators created a fake profile on GEDMatch and uploaded some of the DNA that they had from a 1980 crime scene. After sifting through the data, they were able to find 24 of his relatives who had uploaded their genetic information to GEDMatch. This resulted in identifying their suspect, Joseph DeAngelo. The process they used is called reidentification, and it can be used on genetic information that is stripped of all personal information to locate the individual and match them to their personal information. [50]

Overall, explore why you want the genetic information. Is it to locate distant relatives or to set your mind at ease about a disease many people in your family have had? Once you have the information, what will you do with it? Always speak to a genetic counselor before doing genetic testing to gain a deeper understanding of the pros and cons of genetic testing. As technology advances, the day will come when your genetic information will be able to be reidentified. Is that a risk you are willing to take?

NURSING KNOWLEDGE

A genetic counselor is an expert who can list the pros and cons of getting genetically tested. While this chapter highlights some information to educate you, I would still urge you to seek a professional's opinion before getting genetically tested.

CHAPTER 12

Value-Based Care: The Next Phase of Health Care

We are a nation of consumers and when we buy something, we judge the quality of the goods we are buying, or at least we should. No one wants to buy a car that they continually have to take back to the dealership for service. So why shouldn't health care operate in the same fashion? After all, you can't take back a nasty scar after a botched appendectomy operation. You need to do your work on the front end.

As health care costs continue to climb, experts have realized that fee-for-service isn't going to be a sustainable model. There has to be an essential shift in health care, and that essential shift is quality outcomes. A quality outcome is the measure of the impact of a health care service, such as how many patients contract or receive an infection while in the hospital or die due to complications from surgery. The American Healthcare System is heavily regulated by various regulatory bodies who often cite organizations for inadequate care and often decrease or stop reimbursement payments for health care organizations lacking in positive quality outcomes. Value-based care incentivizes health care organizations to provide quality care at a decreased cost. This is important for you to understand because this is how care is going to be delivered in the future.

Value-based care focuses on all aspects of care coordination. In the fee-for-service model, your medical care is frequently provided in silos, meaning your doctor isn't speaking to other members of your health care team. Communication with the entire health care team would enable everyone to see your complete health care picture together. Value-based care incentivizes the health care team to communicate to keep you out of the hospital. If done correctly, this will reduce the costs, improve the quality of your care and provide greater incentives to the health care team when they can meet the goal.

The Business Case for Value-Based Care

Let's explore the business model for a minute. In the fee-for-service model, the doctor or health care organization doesn't get paid unless you present with a symptomatic illness. They make their money treating sickness in a reactive manner. The medical staff gets paid according to the volume of patients they see, not necessarily on how well the patients do. In value-based care, they are incentivized to keep you healthy and out of the hospital. That means if the health care organization or doctor's office is collecting $1,000 a month per head for each patient from the insurance company payor, the health care organization or doctor's office gets to keep the profit if they can keep you out of the hospital. When you show up at the hospital with an illness, you're costing your provider part of their incentive. Instead of bringing the health care organization or doctor's office in revenue in a fee-for-service model, you are costing the health care organization or doctor's office revenue. This should result in the health care team keeping you as healthy as possible to remain profitable. Everyone wins. You remain healthier with a team focused on keeping you as healthy as possible, and they profit from keeping you healthy. It's a radical shift from getting paid for treating your illness. This model incentivizes the health care team to collaborate on your care, which has been difficult to accomplish in a fee-for-service payment structure. Value-based care is administered through Accountable Care Organizations (ACOs) using bundled payments, which is proactive care as it causes your care team to set up and maintain a line of communication about your care.

Value-based care has the potential to shift us from a siloed or isolated provider-based payment model to one that is patient focused. This holistic look at your health care means greater responsibility by the health care team and the patient to be a part of the process. Remember in the old day's providers knew best and patients were expected to accept their opinion. In value-based care, the patient and the health care team must work together to obtain the greatest quality outcomes. In 2018 Seema Verma the administrator of the Centers for Medicare and Medicaid Services (CMS) said "We will not achieve value-based care until we put the patient at the center of our healthcare system." [51] Here is an interesting story about value-based care and bundled payments.

Value-Based Care and Bundled Payments in Action

Bundled payments refer to one procedure, in this case, a hip surgery, in which many different health care players receive reimbursement based on the outcome of the patient. The surgeon, nurses, lab technicians, anesthesiologist, the rehabilitation group, and possibly home care are included in this bundle. My brother-in-law had a hip replacement at his local hospital and did fine. He was discharged to home relatively soon after the procedure. While at home he began to develop heart palpitations and chest pain. My sister rushed him to the emergency department, fearing that he was having a heart attack. In the emergency department, they were able to figure out that my brother-in-law's illness was a reaction to the opioid pain medication that he was on and not necessarily anything cardiac related. My brother-in-law never consumes alcohol, let alone had taken opioid pain medication before. They changed his pain medication and discharged him back home and instructed him about what to do if his symptoms occurred again.

The next day my sister was contacted by the group who did the hip surgery. They wanted to send a nurse out to check on my brother-in-law and schedule a time for a couple of days later where they could come back out and check on my brother-in-law again. My sister and I discussed what occurred and she said to me, "Oh it's so wonderful that they would come out and check on him and it's all free! These nurses come out to make sure he's doing OK, take his vital signs and they don't charge us anything."

I explained to my sister that this service was not free at all. Because my brother-in-law went to the emergency department and was part of a bundled payment reimbursement program, the bundle payment group had to absorb the cost of the visit. I explained to her that the nurses were serving the best interest of the accountable care organization who administered the bundled payment plan of my brother-in-law's hip replacement, even though I would consider this response to be a patient-centric approach. It was interesting to see this from the patient's perspective in response to the amount of attention that was given to them after his surgery and on their road to recovery.

Value-Based Care and Revenue

To understand why we need to drive this change, value-based care is more patient focused than the fee-for-service model. Let's take a look at what occurred during the pandemic of 2020. A report by the American Hospital Association stated that healthcare systems and hospitals would lose 320 billion dollars in the year 2020. This makes sense as patients who were going to have elective surgeries didn't want to be anywhere near a hospital where COVID-19 patients were being treated, so they elected to reschedule those surgeries until later. In a fee-for-service model, where hospitals are reimbursed by the volume of patients they care for, this model can be devastating to their bottom line. As the volume decreases so does the revenue.

This revenue decrease did not occur in organizations using a value-based model. This is because their income isn't dependent on the volume of patients that they see. They receive the same amount of money per patient regardless of whether that patient accessed the healthcare system. In the fee-for-service model, many hospitals had to furlough employees to cut costs and remain viable. While value-based care can drive down costs and improve outcomes, it can also protect a health care organization during an economic downturn or a pandemic. This makes the approach much more palatable to organizations and insurance companies, so hopefully, the shift to value-based care will occur more rapidly. [52]

While it looks promising, how do we know the value-based care model can drive down costs and improve health outcomes? Humana recently released a report which revealed 2.41 million Humana individual Medicare Advantage (MA) members that received care from primary care physicians in a value-based model experienced better health outcomes, lower costs, and more preventive care. An estimated $4 billion in covered medical expenses would have been incurred by these members if they had been under a fee-for-service model. They also found that these members in value-based care arrangements went to the emergency department 10.3 percent less (90,500 fewer visits) and had a 29.2 percent lower rate of hospital admission (165,000 fewer admissions).

The Chief Executive Officer (CEO) of Humana believes value-based care models have a better impact on addressing physical health, behavioral health, and social health care related needs. This is certainly a more holistic approach to meeting the community member where they are. [53]

Social Determinants of Health Care

Perhaps one of the greatest advantages of value-based care is the ability to deliver care equally. Too often it's the dollar that counts in health care. If you have more money, then you receive better health care because you can afford to pay for high priced prescriptions or specialists. During the pandemic of 2020 life expectancy rates fell from 78.8 years to 77.8 years overall. This is significant because the last time a drop of this magnitude occurred was during World War II. But as we drill into these numbers we find an eight month drop for white Americans, a one year, nine month drop for Hispanic Americans, and a two year, seven month drop for Black Americans. Delivering health care equally across our society is the right thing to do. This has the potential to occur in a value-based care model. [54]

Social determinants of health care are the economic and social factors that impact individuals and groups of individuals. Simply put, these are health promoting factors found in your everyday life, where you work and live. Different groups of people have different risks. This is due to many factors, but usually, the biggest one is wealth. People who have more income tend to have better health outcomes. To be clear, we are not talking about genetic risk factors. Most often the distribution of health care is controlled by state or federal government policy, and little to no attention is paid to the effects of the policy on social determinants of health care. The World Health Organization states, "This unequal distribution of health damaging experiences is not in any sense a 'natural' phenomenon but is the result of a toxic combination of poor social policies, unfair economic arrangements [where the already well-off and healthy become even richer and the poor who are already more likely to be ill become even poorer], and bad politics." [55]

Research shows us that only 10-20 percent of an individual's health is attributed to medical care. The research estimates that

40 percent of health care is due to health behaviors such as making the right food choices, abstaining from illicit drugs, smoking, and alcohol, as well as increasing your physical activity level. Another 40 percent is attributed to social circumstances, such as housing, food insecurity, transportation, or other barriers, which can result in poor health outcomes and increased health care costs and utilization of the healthcare system.

Social determinants of health care are a big focus as we move to a value-based model. This is because our society does not treat each member equally. A good example of that occurred during the COVID-19 crisis in which those people with a college education were shifted to working from home. Those in the service and hospitality industries still had to work out in the community to earn their wages, putting themselves at higher risk every day. Many other people were laid off from their jobs, which meant they were at risk of losing their employment based health care insurance.

To move to a truly value-based care model, discrepancies such as socioeconomic status have to be addressed. Research from the National Research Council places the United States lowest in terms of life expectancy out of 17 high income countries. Health care disparities take part of the blame. The variation in life expectancy across the country is concerning.

To impact social determinants of health care, you first have to understand what the problem is and where it's occurring. Second, you have to be willing to make an impact on the issues you find. Insurance companies who are responsible for Medicaid populations have a vested interest in addressing that inequality. That inequality affects their bottom line. Sadly, this is not a humanity driven issue. The cold fact is the driving factor for most health care business models is money instead of health. As an example, an Institute of Healthcare Improvement (IHI) presentation noted a 10 year life expectancy increase for people who lived on the Upper East Side of

Manhattan than those who lived five miles away in the South Bronx. Until these discrepancies are narrowed, there can be no equitable health care in this country. [56]

Addressing Social Determinants of Healthcare

Fortunately, several tools have been developed to help us discover issues that may be affecting the health care of a community. Blue Cross in California began developing a tool called the Neighborhood Health Dashboard. Coordinating multiple sources of data, it brings in data from the various sources to be used in determining the problem areas in a community. This data, which can be publicly accessed using the internet, is broken down by zip code to see what kind of social issues are affecting different communities.

Tools such as these should aid in advancing public health by creating transparent views of health care discrepancies. This tool is free to the general public and allows disparate organizations to look at the health outcomes and how to use preventative care. This helps hospitals, doctors, policymakers, and community leaders understand the needs of a community by enabling them to address their specific problems. [57]

One way to use a dashboard to improve community health is addressing food insecurity. Say, you use the dashboard for a certain zip code, where you can see the majority of the population lives below the poverty line with children in a school system who are complaining of being hungry while at home. This allows community leaders and health care advocates to grasp the root cause of the problem and look at possible solutions to improve community health. Perhaps this is a good location for a food bank or farmers market that sells fresh vegetables at a subsidized price.

In another example of making data publicly available, if the community had a large flu outbreak the year before, a health care organization could set up a clinic and provide free flu shots to the members of the community as a preventative measure. There are many creative ways to use the data to address social determinants of health which should produce better health care outcomes.

Executing on a Plan to Address Social Determinants of Health Care

It's not enough just to have the data. You have to be able to execute a plan that meets the community's needs. The Centers for Medicaid and Medicare Services (CMS) are attempting to do that through the use of their Accountable Health Community model, which is being used to link clinicians with community concerns to produce better health care outcomes. This is a study of 29 organizations across 21 states running over a five year period.

The study showed the number one cause of social issues associated with health care outcomes was food insecurity. The recent pandemic exacerbated food insecurity issues as with much of the country becoming unemployed, having enough to eat became a major issue. It is amazing in the world's richest country that we still have people who don't know where their next meal is coming from. 750,000 people were screened for this study, which revealed 34 percent had food insecurity issues, 25 percent were concerned with housing, 23 percent had transportation problems, 15 percent had utility issues and 3 percent were concerned about safety. Once their concerns were identified, the community members were referred to Accountable Health Community navigators for interventions. The navigators identify and prioritize accessibility gaps in community services to develop a targeted, scalable project to make services easier to access. [58]

In a fee-for-service model, community members are treated only when they are ill. Factors such as food insecurity, lack of transportation, and violence in the home were never really considered to be a part of their overall health care. In a value-based care model, these factors are very important to treating the individual community member holistically and setting them on a personal path to wellness. Using the vast amounts of data that we can generate to study the problem and models, such as the Accountable Health Community work that the CMS is doing, should drive down costs and increase health care outcomes.

If you find yourself living in a poverty zone or experiencing any of these social determinants of health care factors, you now know there are agencies within the community that can assist you. If you find yourself in the hospital or visit the emergency department, you can ask for a consult with a social worker who will be able to help get you pointed in the right direction. You can access a community resource by doing a quick internet search to see the options available in your community. It's been a long time coming, but social determinants of health care must be considered when addressing a community member's or communities' overall health care outcomes.

Value-based care is a game changer. When you have a set amount of money on each life covered in a value-based care model, you are incentivizing your care team to be innovative in the way they keep you healthy and at home. Social determinants of health care play a major factor in how you are cared for. This will force the health care team to look at your situation holistically and drive an individualized plan of care to meet your needs to keep you healthy. It's a win-win for the payors, the health care team, and the patients.

CHAPTER 13

Consumerism in Healthcare

As patients or consumers learn more about health care, they want to participate in a shared decision model. Maybe this is one reason you are reading this book. This approach will require a culture change in the medical community. Remember earlier in the book when I referred to the three phases of health care? The first phase was: the doctor knows best. Anything the doctor told you to do, you did without question. The second phase was using evidence-based research to standardize your health care. This approach followed the assumption that if you were having hip surgery, the majority of patients followed the same course of treatment with minor patient specific tweaks. The third phase is using machine learning and artificial intelligence to augment medical knowledge and hopefully produce better health care outcomes. Consumerism in health care spreads across all three phases in various forms. As more medical information becomes available to the general public, we will see consumerism in health care rise.

Health care consumerism is generally defined as people proactively using trustworthy, relevant information (not everything on the internet is trustworthy and relevant) and the appropriate technology to make better informed decisions about their health care options. This will occur both inside and outside the clinical setting. [59] Simply put, you as the individual should be taking an active part in your health care through personal accountability and shared decision making with your health care team.

Here is an example of the old American Healthcare System, where the doctor knows best and we are not supposed to question anything they tell us. Many of my older relatives adhered to this medical culture—except for my uncle. It may be the reason he is still around at 86. My uncle has a cardiac history, and one day he didn't feel right. He went to his cardiologist and told him something felt off. The cardiologist told him to go home and they would monitor it. My uncle pushed back and demanded to be examined further.

The cardiologist reluctantly took my uncle in for an exploratory cardiac catheterization. In that procedure, they enter your vessels from an artery in your thigh or your wrist and take a look at the vessels inside your heart. The cardiologist found his left anterior descending (LAD) artery was 95 percent occluded, meaning the artery was 95 percent plugged with plaque. In the medical field, we call this the "widow maker" because this is the main artery supplying blood to your left ventricle or chamber of your heart. The left ventricle creates the contractions to pump blood through your body. If it totally occludes, you are probably going to die.

In my uncle's case, he was very close to total occlusion. That's why he felt a little off. If he hadn't been so firm with his cardiologist, he could have had a massive heart attack. The moral of the story is: you know your body best and should partner with your health care team to promote your health care.

Health care consumerism is needed, as in the past if you had a bad experience while being a patient, you had no way to share that information to help the hospital or care provider improve. The government recognized this and put in place surveys called the Hospital Consumer Assessment of Healthcare Providers and Systems (HCAHPS) scores. These are mandatory for all hospitals and affect their financial reimbursement. More importantly, the Centers for Medicare and Medicaid (CMS) uses this information to rate hospitals, which they then publish on their website. Using this quality information allows you to make an informed decision about the doctor or hospital you allow to care for you.

The Problem with the Top-Down Approach

In my experience, the medical community had a disconnect for many years in which they did not involve the patient in their care. A good example of that was when the regulatory bodies instituted care plans for patients. A care plan is a list of interventions centered around the patient's diagnosis or problem. The idea was correct, getting the whole care team's input for the patient's progress, but we left out one very major detail— the patient. We as a health care team would stand outside the patient's room discussing the patient's health care plan but not including the patient or their caregivers in that discussion. Care planning or patient involvement is very important because then they have skin in the game.

For example, if you're taking care of a patient who has congestive heart failure (CHF) and you are discussing changing their medications to improve their health. The medical team asks the patient what their goal is for the day. This goal becomes very important if you want the patient to progress. When the patient states a goal, such as I want to walk ten feet without being short of breath, then the care team has a goal to work on together and by care team I mean including the patient and their caregiver. I don't know when the last time you were in a hospital as a patient, but usually there isn't much to do. Most patients decrease their activity levels while waiting for their care team or quietly visit with family and friends. The patient has little incentive to get up and move, and patients need to get up and move to make progress and be discharged from the hospital or rehab facility. Having consumers/patients as active members of the health care team usually helps them progress more quickly.

Here is an example of another uncle of mine. My uncle has electrolyte issues and had to take phosphorus supplements which made his medical condition fragile. He was also on many medications and without those medications, he would not have survived. He was in the hospital and his attending doctor who knew him well was called away for a family emergency. The doctor covering my uncle's attending doctor came into the ICU, as my uncle recently had open heart surgery and he also suffered a small stroke. He told my aunt and uncle he was going to look at my uncle's medications and would return shortly.

My aunt left the room to go over the medications with the covering physician. He asked her about some of the medications, and she explained the rationale for each one. Then he asked her why my uncle was on Lithium. My aunt replied, "He is on Librium, not Lithium." The covering doctor retorted, "No, it says right here he is on Lithium." My aunt became frustrated and replied, "You can't give him Lithium. That will kill him!"

The covering doctor then told my aunt to step away and be quiet. She did neither. She instead put her foot down until this doctor understood that she meant business. By that time, his attending doctor returned from his family emergency, and he straightened the situation out. If my aunt hadn't been there to be an advocate for my uncle, my uncle could have easily been a victim of the American Healthcare System.

NURSING KNOWLEDGE

It is *strongly* recommended that you have a loved one with you at all times in the hospital. Someone who is familiar with your health care history. In times such as a pandemic, stay connected to your loved ones health care team if you can't be bedside with your loved one.

If a doctor is not listening to you when you try to give them information about your or a loved one's health care, you have the option of asking for another doctor. If you're in the hospital, you can always find the Nurse Manager of the unit you or your loved one is on during the day. If the situation occurs during off hours, you can find the Charge Nurse or have the Nursing Supervisor called to the floor. Do not tolerate someone who isn't listening to you and will not partner with you in your health care. This is an old school mentality that is harmful to patients.

Due to the uptick in consumerism in health care many hospitals have added an additional position called the Chief Client Experience Officer. Health care organizations are beginning to understand that many of the consumers they serve can shop for where they will receive their care. There is much more emphasis on the consumer experience from beginning to end. One organization that recognized this was Providence Saint Joseph's Health. They believe their Cancer Center is chosen for reasons that have nothing to do with the treatment. The patients know they will work with the same nurse throughout their course of treatment, and their families will also receive care. They are introduced to alternative therapies, as it's a consumer-oriented choice. This consumer-friendly approach creates loyalty and patient satisfaction. [60]

Another trend in health care is the rise of clinics set up in retail environments. Patients no longer have to go to the doctor's office and wait an hour or more to be seen. They can sign up for an appointment right down the street from where they live at their local Walmart, Walgreens, or CVS. Here they can be seen by a nurse practitioner. There has also been some work done allowing these consumers to be seen by Telehealth, using technology in these retail clinics. All this points to a trend in which the average health care consumer is willing to go to different venues to receive care that is more convenient for them. Some experts in health care are predicting that hospitals could be drastically reduced in size over the next decade as care is given in smaller environments at a decreased cost. [60]

The Impact of Technology

No chapter on health care consumerism would be complete without discussing how technology plays into this process. As we saw earlier, your smartphone can enable you to be a better health care consumer. You can access your patient portal for relevant information and labs. You can download your medical records to an app, although you do need to beware of the risks involved, as we discussed before. And savvy health care providers are using alerts that fire to your smartphone to remind you of your next medical or dental appointment or your yearly flu shot. This is a brilliant strategy by hospitals and health care providers in an attempt to keep your business.

These days we use our electronic calendars and alerts to keep us scheduled and on time for appointments. The smart health care organization knows this and alerting us is an invaluable tool to keep your business. Health care organizations do not want you going to your local retail pharmacy to obtain your care, and strategies like these to keep the health care consumer informed of their preventative care will make them dependent on their current health care provider. This is coupled with working on the client experience, such as decreasing wait times in your local doctor's office or emergency department, to add brand loyalty and keep you coming back. Health care consumers tend to demand they get the same efficient treatment in health care as they do for other major purchases.

Doing your research on your health care is important. That research can be on trusted internet sites such as WebMD or interviewing your older relatives. Being involved in your care is essential to having great health care outcomes.

I recall a conversation with yet another one of my uncles who had high cholesterol. He told me that genetically as a family we were predisposed to both high blood cholesterol and high intestinal cholesterol. Not a lot of people know that there are two different ways in which cholesterol enters your body. One is from your gastrointestinal (GI) tract, and the other is absorbed in your bloodstream. When my cholesterol medication was not working optimally, I sat down with my provider and let him know about my family's genetic predisposition to GI cholesterol. He then prescribed me a drug that would attack the cholesterol in my GI tract as well as continuing the cholesterol medication for my high blood cholesterol. This brought my cholesterol down significantly and using these combined medicines we were able to get my high cholesterol under control.

This is an example of consumerism in health care, as I had relative and accurate information to bring to my health care provider which resulted in our making a medical decision together which produced a better health care outcome. Remember, you as a health care consumer know your body better than anyone else.

CHAPTER 14

How to Be Your Best You

I was 21 years old when I decided to stop smoking. You might think if I was only 21, I hadn't been smoking for very long but that was far from the truth. I started smoking cigarettes at 13 years old and was a two-pack-a-day smoker for eight years. When I decided to quit smoking, I did the research and knew the actual physical withdrawal was about 10 days and the mental withdrawal was about 30 days. This was important because when I started craving a cigarette after 12 hours, I knew if I smoked one I would have to relive that 12 hours all over again. That 30 day mark is important because if you can change your habits for 30 days, you stand a much better chance of making a lifelong commitment to the new healthy behavior. This is true in any bad habit you are trying to kick whether it be cigarettes, alcohol, or a bad relationship.

Yet in my quest to quit cigarettes I turned to an alternative bad habit and began to eat like a crazy man. I gained 50 pounds in a relatively short period of time because what I did was replace my craving for cigarettes with food. It was great that I got off the cigarettes, but now I was huffing and puffing to get up a flight of stairs. This left me with a new and different problem. I accomplished losing the weight over a period of a year with a lot of work. I was working the night shift, jogging when I got home in the morning, eating less, and taking control of my health.

That is key to not being a victim of the American Healthcare System. If you are the best you that you can be and work alongside your clinical team to ensure a good quality of life, you will not need to access the healthcare system as often. Sure, certain events like an abscess on your chest will force you to go to the emergency department, but they should be less frequent. You should start a winning streak of your own. Every day you're faced with choices that will impact your health care, so it's time to make the right ones.

Making Good Choices

Good health is not an accident. It's something that you work at every day! From the time you wake up to the time you go to bed, you are faced with a series of choices about your health. Let's take breakfast, for instance. You could have a healthy bowl of steel-cut oatmeal or a Krispy Kreme donut. These minor choices impact your health. If you had a healthy bowl of oatmeal, you would feel satisfied and take in fewer calories than if you went for the donut. Donuts will load you with carbs and sugars, which will make you tired by mid-morning and spike your insulin levels, which will make you hungrier sooner. Although a donut may currently be your chosen breakfast, try not eating it for 30 days and see if you feel better.

NURSING KNOWLEDGE

The 30 day concept or challenge can be life altering. If you want to make a health care or lifestyle change set a goal for yourself to stop the behavior for thirty days. Don't be hard on yourself if you fail, just reset and start your 30 days over.

Another daily choice is your activity level. You can choose to just sit on the couch with a bag of chips and binge watch Netflix, or you could commit to walking for an hour every day. These are choices that only you can make, but they definitely impact your health.

With all the medical knowledge we have acquired, I find it curious that the current theory of body positivity is so widely accepted. This may not be politically correct, but as a health care professional, I feel it is important to address the dangers of the body positivity movement. Everyone tiptoes around this delicate issue, but I am just going to do a cannonball into this pool. The body positivity movement is the acceptance of your own body even if you are morbidly obese. While I think people should be comfortable in their own skin, this is a dangerous mindset for health care, as it sends the message that it's OK to not work on improving your health. Accepting the way you are takes the accountability away from the patient, and they no longer participate in improving their health care journey.

Mostly, this is a young person's mindset. What they don't see is the wear and tear on their bone joints from years of being morbidly obese. Not to mention the risk of developing diabetes, strokes, and even heart attacks from the physical stress on the body from carrying this excess weight. You don't see many morbidly obese 70 or 80 year olds preaching body positivity. That's because most morbidly obese people don't reach a ripe old age. Again, that's a health care choice and with every choice comes ramifications.

Get a Yearly Check-up

I cannot stress how important it is to get a yearly check-up. A lot of people think, "I feel fine, so therefore I don't need to see a doctor," but all the research shows that preventative care is a way to catch a disease early. I had a friend who was a nurse and was very busy caring for others in a nurse leadership position. I called her when I was going to start my doctorate program, as I wanted her to be my mentor. During the course of the conversation, I noticed she was coughing a lot. Being a nurse, I told her I didn't like the sound of her cough. I was getting ready to go on a vacation with my wife, and I asked her to please go to the doctor and get herself checked out. Yet this self-sacrificing person was working 12 to 14 hours a day, role modeling leadership, and not caring for herself as well as she should have.

When I returned from my vacation, she called me and asked me to sit down. She had indeed gone to see the doctor and they did a chest X-ray. She knew something was up because the X-ray tech, whom she'd known for many years, acted funny and then broke down and cried. They immediately read the X-ray and informed her that her lungs were full of cancer. Not just cancer but stage 4 cancer, which is the worst you can have. It turned out that she had cancer in other parts of her body also. She was a fighter and lived a lot longer than the doctors originally told her she would, but eventually, the cancer took her life.

Your yearly doctor's appointment is essential to your health care. Early discovery of cancer or any other disease gives you a much greater chance to beat it. We all have a limited time on this earth. Let's try to stay around for as long as possible with a good quality of life.

Choosing Food Wisely

Without taking a deep dive into nutrition, I will tell you that the Food and Drug Administration (FDA) has allowed foods to enter our food supply that are not good for you. The first is high fructose corn syrup, or fake sugar, which is a manufactured concentrated form of corn syrup that is ten times sweeter than cane sugar. Reading the labels of anything that you're going to eat is very important, as high fructose corn syrup will affect your health. In fact, anything you consume should not list sugar or high fructose corn syrup within the first five ingredients. If it does, stay away from it.

The first ingredient listed on a label makes up the majority of the product. High fructose corn syrup was invented as a cheap alternative to sugar. It has been linked to obesity, fatty liver disease, and heart problems and it is not natural like sugar is. Glucose is the simplest form of sugar. Fructose needs to be broken down to glucose, which is stored in the liver. High fructose corn syrup triggers a reaction in your body that causes you to want to eat more, as it increases hunger and sugar cravings and provides no nutritional value. High fructose corn syrup is something that every reader of this book should stay away from and sugars, in general, should be limited. It can be found in ketchup and barbeque sauce as well as a variety of other foods. I can't stress enough that reading the ingredient labels of any food you are going to consume is very important.

Another ingredient to avoid is partially hydrogenated or hydrogenated oils. These contain trans fats, which are very bad for you. One of the culprits is artificial creamers that are available at coffee shops, restaurants, and grocery stores. These should be avoided at any cost. Use real cream because it's much better for you than using hydrogenated oils. While I could make many more points about nutrition, there are a plethora of nutrition books you can read. For anyone who wants to change their eating habits, I would strongly recommend a consult with a registered dietitian, as they are an invaluable member of the health care team and spend years learning about correct dietary preferences.

NURSING KNOWLEDGE

There are many members of your health care team who are highly specialized. Adding a registered dietician to your health care team will give you an additional resource to access for dietary concerns.

I should also mention Genetically Modified Food (GMO's). They were introduced into the food chain in 1994 as a way to combat world hunger, so very little research has been done on the long-term effects of these foods. GMO foods are any crop or agricultural product altered by biological engineering. This is often done for drought resistance, increased growth, resistance to pests or pesticides, prolonged shelf life, altered textures or flavors, or other economically or commercially desirable characteristics. The GMO industry states that this improves crop yields, which reap additional profits for the food industry. [61]

Many countries outright ban GMOs, such as Russia. Eating GMO foods is very controversial. Studies done on rats yield results such as partially atrophied livers when fed a diet of GMO potatoes. Another study done on rats showed that the babies who were born when female rats were given a diet of GMO soy died within three weeks. Add to this the decreased nutritional value of GMO foods, and I think it's safe to say you should steer clear of GMO products.

You can look for labels that state the product is non-GMO, but the best way to tell how the product was grown is through the use of Price Lookup Codes (PLU) attached to the item. Four-digit codes mean the food was conventionally grown. Five-digit codes starting with the number eight mean the food item is a GMO product. Five-digit codes starting with the number nine mean the food item is organically grown. As an example, a universal code for bananas is 4011, meaning it is conventionally grown. If the PLU were 84011, this would mean it is a GMO product, and if it were 94011, it is organically grown. Reading labels will help you avoid GMO products. [62]

While we're on the subject, let's discuss organic foods. Foods in general, just like health care in general, is a business. In business, shortcuts provide cost savings that will reap the business owner's greater profits. Food is no different. Any food that is not certified organic may have been sprayed with pesticides, which you will consume when you eat these foods. This is why organic food costs more. The growers have to use alternative means to make sure they produce a healthy product. Another benefit to buying organic foods is you won't have to worry about consuming GMO products. Your health is worth the additional cost of organic foods. Again, a registered dietitian would know more about the subject, but it's one change you can make today to keep yourself healthy.

Remember, good health is not an accident or luck. It results from making good food and activity choices. Being in control of your health means being accountable for your health. Doctors and nurses can be great assets on your health care team. It boils down to you making the correct choices and participating in your health care. Show up and be an active member of your health journey. Take it one decision at a time, one day at a time and you'll be on your way to being the healthiest you can be.

CHAPTER 15

Where Do We Go from Here?

Health care is very complex. Beyond your clinical staff are many players in health care who may not have your best interests at heart. It is my hope the knowledge that you gain from reading this book will decrease the possibility of having negative outcomes on your health care journey. Many doctors and nurses enter health care for the right reasons because they feel it is a calling. Yet the businesses that have grown up around the healthcare industry are making millions of dollars off your health care. This is pretty evident, as we are 17th in quality outcomes while spending the most on health care of any other industrialized country. A quality outcome is the measure of the impact of a health care service, such as how many patients contract or receive an infection while in the hospital or die due to complications from surgery. Medical errors are the third leading cause of death in this country. There is much room for improvement, and things are not changing as rapidly as the health care professionals in this country would like. This has a major effect on your health care.

In 1999 the Institute of Healthcare Improvement (IHI) published a paper called "To Err Is Human: Building a Safer Healthcare System," which outlined how dangerous the American Healthcare System truly is. [63] This was eye-opening to a lot of outside observers, but those of us in health care knew this was going on. It simply wasn't discussed. The general public trusted us to take the best care of them as possible, but as a system, we were failing in that endeavor. As clinicians, we knew the doctors who wouldn't be allowed to touch our family members, but we were not at liberty to discuss this hard truth with others in the community. We saw the inefficiencies brought about by hospital administrators who were trying to make a buck off your health care. Our jobs required us to take care of the people, not voice an opinion. In fact, it was very rare that a nurse or doctor was included in making business decisions for the good of the community. Health care decisions were usually made by business people who navigated the intricacies of running health care as a business. Clinicians weren't trained in the business. We were trained to take care of people. But we knew that parasitic entities like the insurance companies and big pharma get away with murder, literally.

Healthcare has been like a secret society. It was often too complicated for the layperson to comprehend the intricacies of what occurred in health care, but they trusted the clinicians to care for them. One of the reasons that I went back to school to obtain my doctorate was because I wanted to have the best knowledge of the healthcare system to make a change. I think it's time to remove the cloak of this secret society and open up the healthcare system so people can understand what's occurring in this country.

In defense of the clinicians, I will say that it's not easy to safely report mistakes in the health care community, although that is beginning to change. In the past when you reported a mistake, you could be subject to punitive retribution. I can remember in my experience when a resident drew up a very concentrated form of a drug that should have been diluted and administered this drug through an intravenous catheter in the patient's arm. This action caused the patient's death, yet it was the nurse who was punished for handing him the concentrated vial of medicine. The resident was never disciplined, even though as clinicians we are expected to check the labels of the drugs that we give before we administer them. In an environment like that, it was difficult to report mistakes without fear of retribution or even the loss of your job. It's my hope you learned some of the essential skills necessary to navigate the American Healthcare System and avoid being a victim of it.

Rethinking the Public Health Structure

I think we need to examine how the CDC, CMS, HHS, FDA, and other entities that are looking out for our health care are tied to America's political structure. What I have learned is it's not always easy to effectively teach patients when you're tied to an organization or government entity. The conversation that I had with the woman at the grocery store about her surgeon I couldn't have had at the hospital while I was prepping this woman for surgery. It would have been totally inappropriate and the health care organization that I worked for would not have appreciated my honesty. The doctor with the bad hands and poor judgment who missed medical changes that caused several people to die, I couldn't have taken out a full-page ad in the newspaper advising people to stay away from this dangerous surgeon even though that may have been the right thing to do. While many of us knew what was going on we didn't have the platform to make any real changes. This has been something that I've struggled with within the healthcare system for years. This is why I believe that we need to have a different platform because clearly what we are doing currently is not effective.

I would propose we should start a patient advocacy platform. A platform that is independent of the government in which we use clinical knowledge such as a nation's Chief Nurse/Doctor to disseminate information to people. This platform would put a patient's needs first and foremost. This platform could also lobby against the insurance companies over inflated costs and poor insurance coverage and big pharma's high-priced medications. We need someone who looks out for us as health care consumers without a hidden agenda.

Will it require a second pandemic and more deaths to organize and pursue drastically needed changes in the healthcare system?

59 percent of all Americans believe our healthcare system needs to be reinvented. [64] In the introduction I spoke about why an educated nurse is the perfect person to lead you through the intricacies of the American Healthcare System. Hopefully, you are now thinking that as a team we can make this system better. When doctors, nurses, and the other disciplines in health care confer about a patient's condition, we can often make improvements. With the patient's involvement, we can make better improvements. Imagine what we could accomplish as a nation collectively wanting to make a change. If that occurs, there's no stopping us from having the best healthcare system in the world.

NOTES

Introduction

1 John Hopkins Nursing, *Nurses are the "Most Trusted Profession" for 18 Years in a Row*, January 8, 2020. Accessed July 13, 2020. https://magazine.nursing.jhu.edu/2020/01/nurses-are-the-most-trusted-profession-for-18-years-in-a-row/

Part 1 Staying Safe Inside The Hospital

Chapter 1 What to Know Before You Go To The Hospital

2 Centers for Medicaid and Medicare Services, *Data.Medicare.Gov*, Retrieved from https://data.medicare.gov/

Chapter 2 Tips on Surviving Your Hospital Experience

3 Hall MJ, Levant S, DeFrances CJ. Trends in inpatient hospital deaths: National Hospital Discharge Survey, 2000–2010. NCHS data brief, no 118. Hyattsville, MD: National Center for Health Statistics. 2013. Retrieved from https://www.cdc.gov/nchs/products/databriefs/db118.htm

Chapter 3 Medication Madness

4 John Hopkins Medicine, *Study Suggests Medical Errors Now Third Leading Cause of Death in the U.S.* May 2016, Retrieved from https://www.hopkinsmedicine.org/news/media/releases/study_suggests_medical_errors_now_third_leading_cause_of_death_in_the_us

5 Patient Safety Network, *Medication Errors and Adverse Drug*

Events, May 2019, retrieved from https://psnet.ahrq.gov/primer/medication-errors-and-adverse-drug-events#:~:text=Nearly%20 5%25%20of%20hospitalized%20patients%20experience%20 an%20ADE%2C,which%20has%20largely%20taken%20 place%20outside%20the%20hospital.

Chapter 4 What You Should Know About Surgery

No References

Chapter 5 Make Your Wishes Known

6 Rowe, Joel, "The Pandemic Should Change the Way We Talk About Dying" *The Atlantic*, July 3, 2020. Accessed July 5, 2020. https://www.theatlantic.com/ideas/archive/2020/07/pandemic-should-change-way-we-talk-about-dying/613618/

Part 2 Paying for Your Care

Chapter 6 Why Your Prescriptions Cost So Much

7 Meller, Abbey & Ahmed, Hauwa. "How big pharma reaps profits while hurting everyday Americans." *Centers for American Progress*. August 30, 2019. Accessed August 15, 2020.https://www.americanprogress.org/issues/democracy/reports/2019/08/30/473911/big-pharma-reaps-profits-hurting-everyday-americans/

8 Wikipedia. "Pharmacy benefit manager". July 23, 2020. Accessed August 23, 2020. https://en.wikipedia.org/wiki/Pharmacy_benefit_management#:~:text=In%201968%2C%20the%20first%20 PBM,in%20the%201980s%2C%20electronically%22.

9 Dodge, Joel. "Pharmacy benefit managers and their role in drug spending." *The Commonwealth Fund*. April 22, 2019. Accessed August 28, 2020. https://www.commonwealthfund.org/publications/explainer/2019/

apr/pharmacy-benefit-managers-and-their-role-drug-spending#:~:text=What%20are%20pharmacy%20benefit%20managers,large%20employers%2C%20and%20other%20payers.

10 Sheng, Ellen. "This app has saved Americans $10 billion on prescriptions so far." *CNBC Disruptor/50.* May 15, 2019. Accessed August 29, 2020. https://www.cnbc.com/2019/05/15/goodrx-app-has-saved-americans-more-than-10-billion-on-prescriptions.html

11 Landi, Heather. "GoodRx files to go public, boasting track record of profitability." *Fierce Healthcare.* August 31, 2020. Accessed September 7, 2020. https://www.fiercehealthcare.com/tech/goodrx-files-to-go-public-boasting-track-record-profitability

12 Japsen, Bruce. "Uber enters home prescription delivery business with NimbleRx." *Forbes.* August 20, 2020. Accessed August 30, 2020. https://www.forbes.com/sites/brucejapsen/2020/08/20/uber-enters-home-drug-delivery-business-with-pharmacy-partner-nimblerx/#557af4c43009

Chapter 7 The Labyrinth of Insurance

13 Healthpayer Intelligence. "How the affordable care act changed the face of health insurance." *Xtelligent HEALTHCARE Media.* June 15, 2016. Accessed August 30, 2020. https://healthpayerintelligence.com/features/how-the-affordable-care-act-changed-the-face-of-health-insurance

14 Holpuch, Amanda. "US health insurers double profits in second quarter amid pandemic." *The Guardian.* August 14, 2020. Accessed September 7, 2020. https://www.theguardian.com/us-news/2020/aug/14/us-health-insurers-coronavirus-pandemic-profit

15 Gee, Emily & Spiro Topher. "Excess administrative costs burden the U.S. healthcare system." *Centers for American Progress.* April 8, 2019. Accessed September 13,

2020. https://www.americanprogress.org/issues/healthcare/reports/2019/04/08/468302/excess-administrative-costs-burden-u-s-health-care-system/

16 Reinhardt, Uwe. "Where does the health insurance premium dollar go?" *JAMA Forum*. April 25, 2017. Accessed September 13, 2020. https://jamanetwork.com/channels/health-forum/fullarticle/2760129

17 Livingston, Shelby. "Health insurer CEOs score big paychecks despite public scrutiny." *Modern Healthcare*. April 22, 2019. Accessed September 13, 2020. https://www.modernhealthcare.com/insurance/health-insurer-ceos-score-big-paychecks-despite-public-scrutiny

18 Shinkman, Ron. "Medicaid enrollment has grown 4.3 million since February, could grow much more." *HealthcareDive*. September 8, 2020. Accessed September 13, 2020. https://www.healthcaredive.com/news/medicaid-enrollment-has-jumped-43m-since-february-could-grow-much-more/584786/

19 Carlisle, Madeleine. "Did you lose your health insurance amid the coronavirus pandemic? You may have other options." *TIME*. May 15, 2020. Accessed September 20, 2020. https://time.com/5837368/lost-health-insurance-coronavirus/

20 Lamberti, Patty. "What to do when you get medical bills you can't afford." *Money Under 30*. January 2, 2020. Accessed September 20, 2020. https://www.moneyunder30.com/paying-medical-bills-you-cant-afford

Chapter 8 Skin in the Game

21 Tozzi, John. "America's largest health insurer is giving apartments to homeless people; A radical fix for the U.S. health-care crisis." *Bloomberg*. November 5, 2019. Accessed October 3,

2020. https://www.bloomberg.com/news/features/2019-11-05/
unitedhealth-s-myconnections-houses-the-homeless-through-
medicaid

22 Almendrala, Anna. "The air ambulance billed more than
his surgeon did for a lung transplant." *KHN*. November 6,
2019. Accessed February 7, 2021. https://khn.org/news/
the-air-ambulance-billed-more-than-his-surgeon-did-for-a-lung-
transplant/

23 Centers for Medicaid and Medicare Services. "How to get the
most out of hospital transparency." Last updated September 30,
2020. Accessed October 27, 2020. https://www.cms.gov/hospital-
price-transparency/consumers

24 Cook, Dan. "How will the CMS's new health care price
transparency rule play out? *Market Insights*. January 27,
2020. Accessed October 27, 2020. https://www.benefitspro.
com/2020/01/27/how-will-the-cmss-new-health-care-price-
transparency-rule-play-out/?slreturn=20200927152442

25 Blase, Brian. "How price transparency would revolutionize
healthcare." *New York Post*. October 12, 2019. Accessed October
27, 2020. https://nypost.com/2019/10/12/how-price-transparency-
would-revolutionize-healthcare/

Part 3 A Better Healthcare System

Chapter 9 Telehealth

26 Telehealth.hhs.gov, *Understanding Telehealth*, Health Resources
and Services Administration. Accessed July 19, 2020. https://
telehealth.hhs.gov/patients/understanding-telehealth/

27 Low, Cherlynn. "Telehealth got a huge boost from COVID-
19. Now what?" *Engadget*, July 16, 2020. Accessed July 19, 2020.

https://www.engadget.com/telehealth-covid-19-coronavirus-policy-accessibility-150057795.html

28 Telehealth.hhs.gov, *US States and Territories Modifying Requirements for Telehealth in Response to Covid-19*, Health Resources and Services Administration. July 17, 2020 Accessed July 19, 2020. https://www.fsmb.org/siteassets/advocacy/pdf/states-waiving-licensure-requirements-for-telehealth-in-response-to-covid-19.pdf

29 Williams, Lauren. "VA secretary touts department's telework, telehealth efforts." July 7, 2020. Accessed July 19, 2020. https://fcw.com/articles/2020/07/07/williams-wilkie-va-updates.aspx

30 Deloitte. "Embracing virtual health results in improved care. "2020. Accessed August 2, 2020. https://www2.deloitte.com/us/en/pages/public-sector/articles/urgency-for-virtual-health-care-adoption.html

31 Ahmed, Erum. "Cerner and Xealth are partnering to infuse EHR with digital care tools." *Business Insider.* August 11, 2020. Accessed August 15, 2020. https://www.businessinsider.com/cerner-xealth-partner-on-ehr-integrated-digital-care-tools-2020-8

32 Benjamin, Regina M. "Medication adherence: Helping patients take their medicines as directed." *Public Health Reports v.127(1).* Jan-Feb 2012. Accessed on August 8, 2020 https://dx.doi.org/10.1177%2F003335491212700102

33 AMN Healthcare. "Home health: Fasted- growing industry faces workforce challenges." 2020. Accessed on August 2, 2020. https://www.amnhealthcare.com/home-health-industry-growth/

34 Johnson, Linda. "Pandemic pushes expansion of 'hospital-at-home' treatment." *AP News.* August 20, 2020. Accessed August 22, 2020. https://apnews.com/37d72aeda92f3964f52c263eb8cd9fee

35 Cohen, Elizabeth. "A silver lining to the pandemic: At-home care helps patients detect life-threatening illnesses." *CNN Health,*

August 22, 2020. Accessed August 23, 2020. https://www.cnn.com/2020/08/22/health/pandemic-silver-lining-home-care-cohen/index.html

36 Holland, Makenzie. "Digital health tools platform attracts HER vendors." *TechTarget*. September 3, 2020. Accessed September 6, 2020. https://searchhealthit.techtarget.com/news/252488559/Digital-health-tools-platform-attracts-EHR-vendors

Chapter 10 Technology

37 Beal, Vangie. "Machine learning." *Webopedia*, Accessed July 25, 2020. https://www.webopedia.com/TERM/M/machine-learning.html#:~:text=One%20of%20the%20most%20well-known%20examples%20of%20machine,data%20mining%20to%20process%20all%20the%20sensor%20data.

38 Dryda, Laura. "How UC San Diego Health, AWS implemented an AI imaging algorithm to detect COVID-19 in 10 days." *Beckers Health IT,* July 10th, 2020. Accessed July 25, 2020. https://www.beckershospitalreview.com/artificial-intelligence/how-uc-san-diego-health-aws-implemented-an-ai-imaging-algorithm-to-detect-covid-19-in-10-days.html

39 Pennic, Fred. "Cerner Integrates Nuance's Virtual Assistant Platform with Millennium EHR to Reduce Physician Burnout." *HIT Consultant.* July 30, 2020. Accessed August 1, 2020. https://hitconsultant.net/2020/07/30/cerner-integrates-nuances-virtual-assistant-platform-with-millennium-ehr/#.XyXIUeuSlPb

Chapter 11 Who Owns Your Healthcare Data

40 Ma, Myles. "Who controls your health data? A guide to your rights." *Policygenius*. September 5, 2018. Accessed August 8, 2020. https://www.policygenius.com/blog/who-controls-your-health-data-a-guide-to-your-rights/

41 Wikipedia. "Health Insurance Portability and Accountability Act." August 8, 2020. Accessed August 9, 2020. https://en.wikipedia.org/wiki/Health_Insurance_Portability_and_Accountability_Act#:~:text=The%20Health%20Insurance%20Portability%20and%20Accountability%20Act%20of,Kassebaum%E2%80%93Kennedy%20Act%20after%20two%20of%20its%20leading%20sponsors.

42 Sydell, Laura. "Storing health records on your phone: Can Apple live up to its privacy values?" *NPR*. February 27, 2019. Accessed august 9, 2020. https://www.npr.org/2019/02/27/697026827/storing-health-records-on-your-phone-can-apple-live-up-to-its-privacy-values

43 Rossignol, Joe. "Apple's health records feature will be available soon to U.S. veterans." *MacRumors*. February 11, 2019. Accessed August 9, 2020. https://www.macrumors.com/2019/02/11/apple-health-records-us-veterans/

44 Landi, Heather. "HHS prioritizing health data access through smartphones in 5-year strategic plan." *Fierce Healthcare*. November 3, 2020. Accessed November 11, 2020. https://www.fiercehealthcare.com/tech/hhs-prioritizing-health-data-access-through-smartphones-five-year-strategic-plan

45 Hardwick, Tim. "Health records firm Epic and about 60 client hospitals object to data sharing rules supported by Apple." *MacRumors*. February 6, 2020. Accessed August 9, 2020. https://www.macrumors.com/2020/02/06/health-records-epic-objects-data-sharing-apple/

46 Leswing, Kif. "Apple and Google will build their coronavirus contact tracing software right into your phone." *CNBC*. September 1, 2020. Accessed September 6, 2020. https://www.cnbc.com/2020/09/01/

apple-google-will-build-coronavirus-contact-tracing-software-right-into-your-phone.html

47 Raths, David. "Premera Blue Cross pays $6.85 million to settle data breach affecting 10.4 million people." *Healthcare Innovation.* September 28, 2020. Accessed October 2, 2020. https://www.hcinnovationgroup.com/cybersecurity/data-breaches/news/21156115/premera-blue-cross-pays-685-million-to-settle-data-breach-affecting-104-million-people?utm_source=HI+Daily+NL&utm_medium=email&utm_campaign=CPS200929065&o_eid=1551J6002234I7V&rdx.ident%5Bpull%5D=omeda%7C1551J6002234I7V&oly_enc_id=1551J6002234I7V

48 Broadwin, Erin. "After you spit into a tube for a DNA test like 23andMe, experts say you shouldn't assume your data will stay private forever" *Business Insider,* February 16, 2019. Accessed July 17, 2020. https://www.businessinsider.com/privacy-security-risks-genetic-testing-23andme-ancestry-dna-2019-2

49 Young, Rich. "What is GEDMatch and why would I want to use it?" *Quora,* June 11, 2016. Accessed July 17, 2020. What is GEDMatch and why would I want to use it? - Quora

50 Broadwin, Erin. "Genetic testing is the future of healthcare, but many experts say companies like 23andMe are doing more harm than good" *Business Insider,* January 12, 2019. Accessed July 17, 2020. https://www.businessinsider.com/future-healthcare-dna-genetic-testing-23andme-2018-12

Chapter 12 Value-Based Care: The Next Phase of Healthcare

51 Rouse, Margaret. "Value-based healthcare." *Healthcare IT.* April 2018. Accessed October 4, 2020. https://searchhealthit.techtarget.com/definition/value-based-healthcare#:~:text=Value-based%20healthcare%2C%20also%20known%20as%20value-based%20

care%2C%20is,better%20health%20for%20populations%2-0at%20a%20lower%20cost.

52 Brady, Michael. "Hospitals will take $320B hit this year, AHA says." *Modern Healthcare.* June 30, 2020. Accessed October 10, 2020. https://www.modernhealthcare.com/finance/hospitals-will-take-320b-hit-this-year-aha-says

53 Leventhal, Rajiv. "Humana touts $4B in 2019 savings due to value-based care agreements." *Healthcare Innovation.* October 8, 2020. Accessed October 25, 2020. https://www.hcinnovationgroup. com/policy-value-based-care/medicare-medicaid/ news/21157584/humana-touts-4b-in-2019-savings-due-to-valuebased-care-agreements?utm_source=HI+Daily+NL&utm_ medium=email&utm_campaign=CPS201008019&o_ eid=1551J6002234I7V&rdx.ident%5Bpull%5D=omeda%7C1551J 6002234I7V&oly_enc_id=1551J6002234I7V

54 Tavernise, Sabrina & Goodnough, Abby. "A grim measure of Covid's toll: Life expectancy drops sharply in U.S. *New York Times.* February 18, 2021. Accessed February 20. 2021. Covid Causes Sharp Drop in U.S. Life Expectancy - The New York Times (nytimes.com)

55 Wikipedia. "Social determinants of health." October 5, 2020. Accessed October 10, 2020. https://en.wikipedia.org/wiki/Social_ determinants_of_health

56 Healthcare Catalyst Editors. "The top 5 2019 healthcare trends." *HealthCatalyst.* March 21, 2019. Accessed October 25, 2020. https://www.healthcatalyst.com/insights/top-5-2019-healthcare-trends

57 Leventhal, Rajiv. "Blue Shield of California unveils neighborhood health dashboard." *Healthcare Innovation.* September 8, 2020. Accessed October 25, 2020. Blue Shield of California

Unveils Neighborhood Health Dashboard | Healthcare Innovation (hcinnovationgroup.com)

58 Raths, David. "Food insecurity is most prevalent social need in accountable health community model." *Healthcare Innovation.* October 7, 2020. Accessed October 25, 2020. Food Insecurity Is Most Prevalent Social Need in Accountable Health Communities Model | Healthcare Innovation (hcinnovationgroup.com)

Chapter 13 Consumerism in Healthcare

59 Carman, Kristin, Lawrence, William & Siegel, Joanna. "The 'New" health care consumerism." *Health Affairs Blog.* March 5, 2019. Accessed October 26, 2020. The 'New' Health Care Consumerism | Health Affairs

60 Compton, Jason. "The consumerism movement in healthcare: How it's making a difference." *Forbes.* April 13, 2018. Accessed on October 26, 2020. https://www.forbes.com/sites/providencedigitalinnovation/2018/04/13/the-consumerism-movement-in-healthcare-how-its-making-a-difference/#6aae88e93095

Chapter 14 How to Be Your Best You

61 Medical Dictionary. "Genetically modified food." *The Free Dictionary by Farlex.* 2009. Accessed 11/1/2020. https://medical-dictionary.thefreedictionary.com/genetically+modified+food

62 Clems. "What is the side effects of GMO foods- 7 proven side effects of GMO foods." *Greenworld Friends.* November 30, 2017. Accessed November 1, 2020. https://greenworldfriends.com/what-is-the-side-effects-of-gmo-foods-7-proven-side-effects-of-gmo-fods

Chapter 15 Where Do We Go From Here?

63 Wikipedia. "Crossing the quality chasm" March 25, 2020. Accessed October 29, 2020. https://en.wikipedia.org/wiki/ Crossing_the_Quality_Chasm

64 Nordlund, Scott. "Industry voices-6 ways of reimagining healthcare in the wake of COVID-19." *Fierce Healthcare.* September 28, 2020. Accessed October 30, 2020. https:// www.fiercehealthcare.com/hospitals/industry-voices-6-ways-reimagining-healthcare-wake-covid-19

AUTHOR BIOGRAPHY

Dr. David Wilcox was born and raised in Syracuse NY. One of his earliest memories was of his grandmother telling him that he would be a doctor one day. It didn't appear that he was following the correct path to that dream as he dropped out of high school and left home at 15 years old. After a failed first marriage that produced a special needs child, Dr. Wilcox knew without a doubt he wanted to be a caregiver. This led him to get his licensed practical nurse (LPN) certification and began his journey into the medical profession. Over the years Dr. Wilcox was a kidney/pancreas transplant nurse as well as an intensive care unit nurse, and emergency department nurse. Later he moved to North Carolina and journeyed into nursing management and became a nursing supervisor while obtaining his bachelor's degree in nursing and master's degree in health administration. He also studied patient throughput or the movement of patients in a hospital and became a patient throughput director. In this role he spoke at many Institute of Healthcare Improvement (IHI) conferences on the creative ways he found to ensure patients being admitted had open beds to go to. Later seeing an opportunity in healthcare information technology (IT) Dr. Wilcox joined a healthcare IT company where he obtained his Lean Six Sigma Black Belt (LSSBB) certification and his doctorate becoming a thought leader in efficient ways to care for patients using technology and clinical buy-in. This journey led him to create this book to reach patients and empower them with the knowledge to better partner with their health care providers.

Dr. Wilcox continues to reside in North Carolina with his wife of 21 years Eva and his three dogs. Being fond of dog rescues, the couple has two English Setters Koni and Ezra, and a beagle rat terrier mix Eleanor Rose. The author can be reached at drdavidwilcox. com.

ACKNOWLEDGEMENTS

When I first had the idea for this book I was finishing a doctorate in executive nursing practice (DNP). When I told my wife Eva about this "idea" of mine to write a book that could reach patients and proactively teach them how to avoid being a victim of the American Healthcare System she replied, "That is absolutely brilliant!" Since then I have had a lot of people believe in this work, my wife of course being my biggest supporter. My aunt Nancy Kubecka took many hours to read through the manuscript to ensure I was addressing the layperson.

I reached out to a literary agent Eric Myers who coached me to self-publish this work and referred me to John Paine who is an independent editor. John guided me through the final edits of the manuscript imparting to me his wisdom from his many years in the publishing business. Eric also suggested I work with Jesse Liebman who assisted me in getting the book's cover designed and getting the book typeset. He also helped me get the book to Amazon so I could reach the readers who need this information.

I have had many people who believed in this work and invested in me over the years. My bonus daughter Natalie Faltyn and my granddaughters Talianna Harris and HarveyAnna Collins have been so supportive of this work. My friend Dr. Jenny Horn who I dragged kicking and screaming into a doctorate program because I didn't want to do it by myself, as well as my mentor and good friend Dr. Jeffery Doucette, who always had my back. I am thankful to the many people who believed in this work and encouraged me to move my dream forward.

Made in the USA
Columbia, SC
27 June 2021

40988558R00104